swimming
for fitness

SECOND EDITION

swimming
for fitness

GEORGE AUSTIN AND JIM NOBLE

A & C Black · London

Published by A & C Black (Publishers)
Limited
35 Bedford Row, London WC1R 4JH

Second edition 1994
First edition 1990

ISBN 0 7136 4040 5

A CIP catalogue record for this book is
available from the British Library

Typeset in 10½pt on 11½pt Linotronic
Electra by ABM Typographics Ltd, Hull
Printed and bound in Great Britain by
Whitstable Litho Printers Ltd,
Whitstable, Kent

Acknowledgements

Illustrations by George Austin.
Photographs by David Marsh. The
authors would like to thank Dr.
Downham for his contribution.

Note: Throughout the book swimmers
are referred to individually as 'he'. This
should, of course, be taken to mean 'he
or she' where appropriate.

Contents

Foreword

I am delighted to be asked to write about this excellent book, particularly because it is just what I want to use myself and also so that I can recommend it to any persons who care about their health, both physical and mental.

Why do I make this point so emphatically? Well, we all need to exercise safely to keep fit and trim. No recreation or activity is better for these goals or safer than swimming. Swimming not only exercises the muscles of our back and chest, but also those of our neck, stomach, arms and legs – and it exercises them without any strain on the heart and lungs. Indeed, it is the only activity that those of us who are disabled or troubled with heart or lung problems should wisely indulge in.

Unlike jogging, squash, cycling and even long-distance (especially hill) walking, swimming is a simple yet consistently healthy form of regular exercise. It can be graded to your own age, level of fitness and requirements and can be simply and inexpensively undertaken in every part of the world. There is no doubt that swimming is one of the most mentally refreshing and relaxing of all physical activities. I know of no better form of exercise. If you are tired, stressed and worried, what is better than a good relaxing swim?

Quite simply, this book can and will guide you to better health. I do recommend you to use it. I certainly shall.

Dr E T Downham
MD, DPM England, FRC Psych.

I
Why swimming is good
for your health

How often do people comment on how much fitter and fresher they feel after a swim than before? Part of the reason for this feeling lies in the enjoyment and benefit of moving about in a completely different medium from land – the water. In water, the body weight is supported in a different way than on land. Movement patterns are quite unlike those of our normal daily life as well as those which are experienced in other sports and recreations. If a change is as good as a rest, then surely swimming can claim to be even better than a rest.

As with most forms of physical recreation, the swimmer is motivated – in this case by water – into lively and energetic activity which in turn generates a state of both physical and mental well-being.

The best kind of exercise is that which benefits all the body systems and functions. There is no activity which does this more effectively than swimming. Demands are made upon the heart, the lungs and the circulatory system and, as the body is in a horizontal position for most of the time, the heart is able to replenish oxygen supplies to the muscles without the need to overcome the force of gravity.

According to heart specialists, it is in our interest to get out of breath at least once a day. The effect of this is to strengthen the heart, to improve circulation and to exercise and strengthen the lungs. How better to achieve this than through swimming, in which the degree of effort can be readily adapted to meet individual needs and tolerance to exercise?

Breath holding, which is frequently required in swimming strokes – especially in underwater swimming – helps to correct any tendency to shallow breathing and to increase the lung capacity. This is known as the *vital capacity*, which is often significantly greater in swimmers than among non-swimmers. This increased vital capacity is of special value in times of physical or mental stress. Moreover, learning to breathe correctly can be a significant factor in reducing tension.

All the main muscle groups in the body are used at some time during swimming. According to your condition, the degree of effort can be increased gradually, enabling the muscles to reach maximum potential and to be kept in good tone. For those who wish to accelerate the process, land-based exercises can be used to supplement the benefits to be derived from swimming. As all the main muscle groups are used in swimming, most forms of exercise are useful; exercises to strengthen the muscles of the arms and legs (which are used in propulsion) are especially beneficial.

For maximum efficiency, muscles need to relax when they are not in use. Movement in water induces relaxation, but maximum benefit is obtained when the water temperature is a comfortable one. As you will see in chapter 3, relaxation is an essential feature of good performance.

During swimming, all the joints in the body are brought into play, ensuring that maximum mobility is developed and maintained. As the legs are not involved in any weight bearing, they can readily be extended from the hips in all directions. There can be few better ways of improving the flexibility of the ankle and foot joints than performing the leg actions in both front and back crawl strokes. And how better to maintain the range of movements possible in the shoulder joint than through the arm actions of these same two strokes?

Poise, or good body position, is an essential feature of all well-performed strokes. Without having to cope with the effects of gravity, the whole body can be stretched out in the water in a way which is unique, and which is beneficial not just to our swimming but also to our physical well-being. It is hardly surprising, therefore, that we are able to emerge from the pool 'walking tall' and feeling glad to be alive!

Above all, swimming should be an enjoyable experience for everyone, regardless of age and ability

In terms of energy 'cost' (how much energy is used), swimming has marked advantages over many other sports or activities. A swimmer needs energy to maintain buoyancy, to propel the body through the water and to fight drag. As using energy means burning calories, it can prove a valuable way of controlling weight. And surely there are few more pleasant ways of doing this than swimming.

Note It is recommended that you do not swim until at least an hour and a half after eating a meal. This is because extra blood supply is needed for the digestive system. Consequently it is inadvisable to divert it to other parts of the body, which would occur if you were to swim too soon after your meal.

2
Making a start

IT may be some time since you last visited a swimming pool or spent half an hour in the water. Perhaps you are a once-a-year swimmer who only resurrects your swimming costume or trunks when you are on holiday, and the sight of the sun sparkling on the sea or the azure blue of the hotel pool tempts you to take the plunge!

You may feel conscious of that embarrassing bulge or those flabby muscles. Take heart: swimming is an excellent way of toning up your muscles and exercising those stiffening joints. What's more, your overall shape will improve with regular swimming sessions if you follow the advice given in this book. In the meantime the spare tyre that you are carrying may actually help you to float better.

Fortunately, as far as equipment is concerned, swimming is one of the cheapest sports in which to participate. Only a costume and towel (plus a cap in some pools) are required, and nowadays the admission charges to most swimming pools are quite modest. If you are a senior citizen or an unemployed person, many local authorities actually encourage you to swim by offering reduced admission fees.

Assuming that you now feel encouraged to take up swimming again, it is worth considering whether the swimming attire you have had for goodness knows how many years might be discarded for something more comfortable and up-to-date. Nowadays there are some very light, attractively styled types of swimwear available from most well-known chain stores or from sports outfitters, at reasonable prices.

Apart from the fact that they are made of quick-drying material such as nylon or lycra, they are snug-fitting and are available in a wide range of colours and designs. You will not only feel better, but you will also look better in a more modern style of swimwear, and that can only be to the good!

As far as caps are concerned, choose one which fits well and feels comfortable. Again, most chain stores or sports shops offer a large selection from which to choose. It is worth paying a little extra to get one that you like and which is likely to last much longer than a cheaper one would.

Unfortunately, the water in some swimming pools can affect your eyes and leave them red and painful after a swim. Should this be the case, it is advisable to purchase a pair of swim goggles which you can wear during your visits and which will prevent any eye irritation. These need to be properly adjusted by means of the straps and the nose piece so that they are not only comfortable but also prevent the seepage of water. Anti-fogging goggles are now available and are worth considering in preference to the normal type. Goggles, of course, have the added advantage of enabling you to see more clearly underwater. If you are short-sighted, it is even possible to have prescription goggles made by an optician; these will enable you to see as clearly as you normally do when wearing glasses or contact lenses.

It is encouraging to note that in more and more pools time is being set aside for adults who wish to swim regularly. The obvious advantages are that this allows them to swim without embarrassment or annoyance during times when there are no boisterous youngsters or competitive swimmers occupying the water. In addition, the quieter conditions are conducive to practice and will allow you to enjoy uninterrupted swimming.

Senior citizens are often catered for separately, even to the extent of having special times set aside during those parts of the day when school-children are not receiving swimming instruction. Occasionally, too, sections are roped off to enable adult swimmers to swim lengths of the pool without hindrance. It is worth making enquires at your local pool to see what is on offer. If you are not fortunate enough to find that special sessions have been allocated to people of your age group, try to choose those times when it is quiet enough for you to practise in relative comfort.

It may be that you feel frustrated with your present standard of swimming because you are able to cover only short distances before feeling fatigued or breathless. If so, by following the advice and suggestions contained in this book, you will find that within a reasonable period of time you will improve in fitness and become much more confident and versatile in the water.

Why not make a start this week – for your health's sake!

3
Some important guidelines

BEFORE we consider the ways in which you can improve your fitness through swimming, let us first look at some important principles which govern performance in all the swimming strokes.

Streamlining

It is important to appreciate that in each of the four main swimming strokes you should try to adopt as streamlined a position in the water as possible. This means that you should try to lie as flat as possible in order to reduce frontal resistance.

Figs 1(*a*) and 1(*b*) illustrate how frontal resistance is increased by failing to adopt a near-horizontal position. A *completely* horizontal position is not desirable because this would result in your legs coming out of the water, with a consequent loss of propulsion.

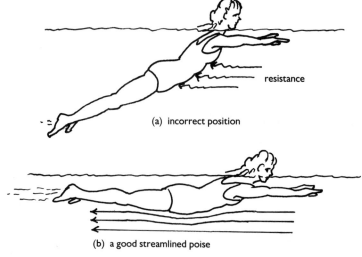

resistance

(a) incorrect position

(b) a good streamlined poise

Fig. 1   Streamlining

Effective breathing

In order for muscles to work efficiently they require a constant replenishment with oxygen. This oxygen is contained in the air, and when we inhale it passes through the lungs and is diffused into the bloodstream. In swimming, breathing has to be a conscious effort, with the air being taken in through your mouth and exhaled through your mouth and nose. Inhalation should occur at regular intervals (normally once each stroke cycle) so that the muscles receive regular supplies of re-oxygenated blood. The exhalation which follows should be a full one so that the carbon dioxide which is created as a result of muscular effort is expelled and the lungs are ready to receive a fresh supply of oxygen-rich air.

Any time spent on developing a good, rhythmic breathing action will pay dividends in the form of improved performance. You should therefore pay particular attention to this aspect of the relevant stroke and try to develop an efficient breathing pattern.

Relaxation within the strokes

One of the hallmarks of a good swimmer is his ability to judge when to apply muscular effort and when to relax those muscles which are not contributing directly to propulsion. This results in a smooth and fluent performance, which often appears effortless to the onlooker. Good examples of when relaxation should occur are in the *recovery* movements of the arms. After the arms have completed their propulsive action they should be moved forwards, *with a minimum of effort*, in readiness for the next propulsive phase.

Showing a good, relaxed arm recovery in front crawl. Inhalation occurs through the mouth, when the face is clear of the water

In front crawl, back crawl and butterfly – in which the arms are recovered over the water – an easy, relaxed, flinging action should be used, with as little muscular effort as possible. In breast stroke, in which the arm recovery takes place in the water, the arms should be moved forwards smoothly and without tension to the glide position, in readiness for the next downward, outward and backward propulsive action.

Unnecessary tension in any stroke means that energy will be needlessly expended and efficiency will be reduced. Learning to relax as much as possible at the appropriate times means you will swim more smoothly and tire less easily than if you are tense.

Efficient leg action

With the exception of breast stroke, the leg action in each of the main swimming strokes is used mainly as a means of maintaining a good, balanced body position; it may also provide a certain amount of propulsion, especially if the swimmer has good, flexible ankles. If the leg action is not effective, this will result in poor poise and subsequently in impaired performance.

Efficient arm action

The arms provide the major source of propulsion in all of the strokes, with the exception of breast stroke. For this reason, special attention should be paid to those practices which are aimed at developing an effective arm action. You are also referred to chapter 8, where there are helpful suggestions for increasing arm mobility and strength.

Warming up

Muscles work most efficiently when they are provided with an adequate supply of blood. Warming up is a way of ensuring that the muscles receive this supply and are therefore able to contract speedily. In addition, the use of appropriate exercise stretches the muscles, tendons and ligaments which are going to be required.

The two main ways of warming up are: light exercise before you enter the water (you can select suitable activities from chapter 8); and swimming itself, especially when you start following the fitness programmes described in chapters 5 and 6. Before athletes in any sport begin a training session or competition you will notice that they first follow a warming-up routine.

Rhythmic pressing exercise. Light exercise before you enter the water can be a valuable part of your warm-up. For more exercises see Chapter 8

Cooling down

It is equally important to cool down after energetic exercise. In swimming this process is achieved by means of a concluding swim at an easy pace, using one or more strokes, and for a given time or distance. (When you make a start on the fitness programme, you will be given guidance on the length or duration of swim to attempt in order to cool down.)

Diet

Normally there should be no need for you to change your eating habits when you start to follow the fitness programme. A balanced diet should be varied and contain meat, fish, vegetables, fruit, dairy produce, eggs and cereals. (Vegetarians will, of course, be aware of appropriate alternatives to some of the above.) Variety is essential, as is a fluid intake to replace the amount lost through normal body functions, i.e. around 1.5 litres daily.

Unless they are prescribed by your doctor, there should be no need for you to take vitamin supplements. A normal diet contains enough of the vitamins and other nutrients which we require for an active, healthy life.

Rest

Unless you are particularly fit, it is best not to follow a vigorous swimming session with a period of similarly strenuous exercise. Instead, it is recommended that you allow your body to recover from the effects of exercise by enjoying a period of quiet relaxation or rest. The amount of sleep that is required depends very much on the individual, but it is obvious that if you do not get enough sleep you will feel disinclined to exercise and will not perform well.

One of the benefits of swimming as a fitness exercise is that if you have worked hard it induces a pleasant feeling of tiredness. In fact, many people who take up swimming remark on how much better they sleep at night after a good workout in the pool.

Exercising during pregnancy

Training advice

During a normal, healthy pregnancy, women can continue swimming if they wish. However, it makes sense to take no risks and to avoid even slightly cold water, viz under 75°F, especially during the third and fourth months of pregnancy. If in doubt, medical advice should be sought before undertaking any form of training or water exercise.

Because of the support offered by the water, swimming is undoubtedly one of the safest and most beneficial forms of exercise to take during pregnancy. This support takes the strain off the lower back, and the continued activity helps to keep the muscles in good shape and to maintain general flexibility.

However, it is most important to be guided by how you feel when considering how much swimming to do. A great deal will depend on your personal fitness and the extent of your previous training. You should certainly not increase your training during pregnancy. Aim rather to keep your swimming at an aerobic level which will not result in an excessive heart rate or a sudden increase in blood pressure.

It is important to appreciate that the ability to train will be affected because of the increasing demands of the expanding uterus and placenta. Since an expectant mother needs to provide oxygen for the foetus as well as for her own body, it becomes more and more difficult to cope with demanding levels of exercise as the baby develops. For this reason, any attempted activities should be moderate in nature and only carried out in appropriate conditions.

Given medical approval, there is no reason why a low level of training should not be continued throughout most of the period of pregnancy. Medical evidence would seem to indicate that those who do so experience fewer problems with delivery and subsequently get back into good shape more quickly.

Ante-natal classes

Nowadays it is becoming increasingly common for ante-natal water aerobics classes to be provided in public swimming pools. Ideally these classes should be professionally supervised, for example by a midwife, and assisted by a qualified physiotherapist. Under carefully monitored conditions, expectant mothers are shown how to perform water exercises which will help to keep them in good shape.

The conditions required for such classes include the exclusive use of a well-heated pool with a comfortable ambient air temperature, where warming up can be carried out gradually. All the water exercises prescribed should be performed at aerobic level, i.e. a level at which oxygen demands can be met by normal breathing and the pulse rate remains at an acceptable level (*Appendix 1, paragraph 2*).

It is most important that medical assistance should be on hand, and that those in charge constantly monitor the participants to ensure that no expectant mothers are allowed to continue exercising if they experience any distress.

One final word of warning. Entry into the pool should always be via the steps during the later stages of pregnancy. Jumping or diving in should **never** be attempted, at any time, as this can be extremely dangerous!

4

Basic starts and turns

THIS chapter has been written for the benefit of any readers who wish to improve their performance through the use of more effective starts and turns but who have little or no previous knowledge of these techniques.

Those who have been involved in competitive swimming in the past will no doubt be familiar with them. Should they wish to develop more advanced skills, such as the 'tumble' turn in front crawl, they are advised to refer to the bibliography for books on competitive swimming.

In this chapter, simple starting and turning techniques are described for each of the four swimming strokes. If practised, they should lead to improved personal performance and greater enjoyment.

As mentioned in chapter 6, time should be set aside in your weekly sessions for practising such skills, and for incorporating them in your swims once you have achieved some degree of proficiency in them.

Unless you are an experienced competitive swimmer, well used to shallow-water starts, you should limit all poolside starts to water of **over 1.5 metres in depth**, because of the risk of neck or spinal injury.

Those wishing to learn how to perform safe shallow-water dives are strongly advised to take the Amateur Swimming Association's Competitive Start Award, possession of which indicates that such competence can be demonstrated. Details of this award may be obtained either at your local swimming pool or by contacting the nearest swimming club.

Basic starting – front crawl, breast stroke and dolphin butterfly

The start in each of these so-called forward strokes follows roughly the same pattern. First there is the *stance*, or starting position, on the poolside or starting block. Next there is the *take-off* and the *flight* through the air. Finally there is the *entry* and the *underwater action*.

The stance

The position to be adopted (*fig. 2*) is one in which you stand at the edge of the pool (or starting block), with feet roughly hip-width apart and toes gripping the edge. Your body should be bent from the waist so that your trunk is almost at a right angle to your legs and your shoulders are ahead of your feet. Your head should be kept in line with your body, allowing you to look forwards and downwards. The whole position should be a comfortable, balanced and relaxed one.

Fig. 2   Basic start: the stance

The take-off

The angle of take-off will depend on the stroke. In front crawl, a shallow type of dive is required, so that as little time as possible is spent underwater. In breast stroke and butterfly you should be aiming for a steeper angle of entry, to enable you to make the most of the underwater glide and permitted arm and leg actions. The accompanying illustrations indicate the difference between the strokes.

After taking up the balanced position on the poolside or block, the knees should be bent; the arms should then be taken backwards and upwards in what is often referred to as 'winding up'. From there, and without pause, the arms should be swung forwards. At the same time a strong backward thrust should be made with your legs to propel you forwards into a fully extended position, with your head between your upper arms and your body as streamlined as possible (*fig. 4*).

Fig. 3 *Showing the front crawl take-off*

Flight

In this fully stretched and streamlined position, your aim should be to adopt the angle which is appropriate to the stroke you intend to swim. In front crawl, as has already been mentioned, a shallow angle of entry is desirable, so the aim should be to keep almost parallel to the water (*fig. 4*). In breast stroke a deeper entry (*fig. 6(b)*) is required so that advantage can be taken of the permissible underwater leg and arm actions. In butterfly, in which any number of leg actions are allowed before surfacing, the angle of flight should be somewhere between the two.

Fig. 4 *The flight phase (front crawl). A shallow angle of entry is required, so aim to keep almost parallel to the water*

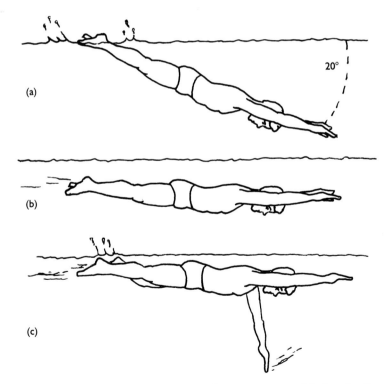

Fig. 5 *Entry (a), glide (b) and underwater action (c) for the front crawl*

Entry, glide and underwater action

It is important to keep your head between your upper arms as you enter the water, and to break the surface with your body still fully streamlined and your hands kept together. In front crawl (*fig. 5*), a shallow glide should follow and your head should be slightly raised to assist your return to the surface. As your speed starts to fall away, first start to kick with your legs and then introduce the first arm action as you return to the surface. In breast stroke (*fig. 6*), first glide, keeping your head still, then use one leg kick, one arm pull and one more leg kick to bring you up to the surface.

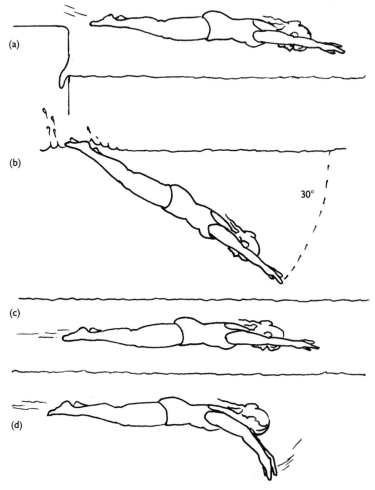

(a)

(b)

30°

(c)

(d)

Fig. 6 *Showing flight (a), entry (b), glide (c) and underwater action (d) for the breast stroke*

In competitive swimming, just one leg kick and one arm action are allowed while your body is underwater, and some part of your head must be above the surface before you take the second stroke.

When swimming butterfly, hold the underwater glide until you feel your speed falling away, after which you may use as many leg actions as you wish but *only one arm action* to enable you to return to the surface.

The back stroke start

In back stroke, the start is made from a position in the water. The stance does not apply to this stroke, but instead there is a 'take up' or position of readiness which should be adopted. There then follows the take-off, flight, entry and underwater glide.

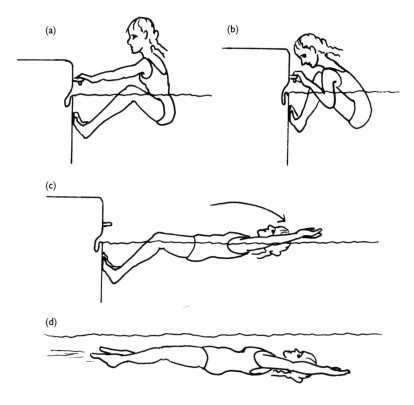

Fig. 7 The back stroke start, showing take-up (a), release (b), flight (c) and underwater glide (d)

Ready position

Stand in the water, holding the rail, trough, or grips of a starting block. Place your feet against the side so that they are below the surface. In this position the feet may be slightly apart and on the same level, or staggered so that one foot is slightly lower than the other. It is important to adopt a secure position so that the feet do not slip (*fig. 7(a)*).

Take-off

Pull your body forwards towards the side of the pool, so that your face is close to your hands. To start, thrust strongly with your legs, at the same time releasing your hands and swinging them in a backward and upward direction so that they are fully stretched and in line with your body as it moves into an extended position (*fig. 7(b)*).

Flight

In this stretched and streamlined position your body should first rise out of the water and then, following a slightly curved path, enter the water in a *shallow* backward dive (*fig. 7(c)*).

Entry

Maintaining this position, aim for a shallow angle of entry so that your body does not go too deep in the water. The impetus of the take-off should enable you to glide for quite a few metres before you feel your speed start to slacken. At this point, start to kick strongly with your legs and raise your head slightly to help you return to the surface (*fig. 7(d)*). As your head breaks the surface, start to pull with one arm and, as soon as you have attained the correct swimming position, continue with the full stroke.

Basic turns

Front crawl

One of the simplest turns to master is called the *throw-away turn*. The sequence is as follows.

As the leading hand touches the end of the pool, bend your arm slightly, turn your body on to its side, tuck your knees up and raise your head (*fig. 8(a)*). This will help to swing your feet into a position where they can be placed firmly against the end of the pool (*fig. 8(b)*). Now push off with your leading hand, allowing your body to sink and bringing your hands together, and use your legs to provide a strong thrust from the wall of the pool (*fig. 8(c)*). Try to adopt a stretched and streamlined position as you move into the glide (*fig. 8(d)*). Just as you did in the other types of starting, begin your leg action as your speed starts to fall away, and on re-surfacing commence the arm action.

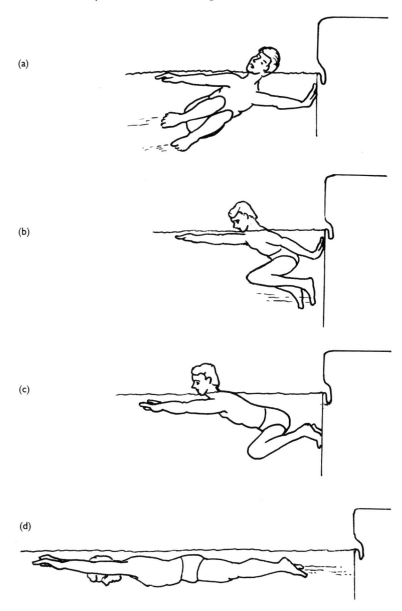

(a)

(b)

(c)

(d)

Fig. 8   The throw-away turn for the front crawl

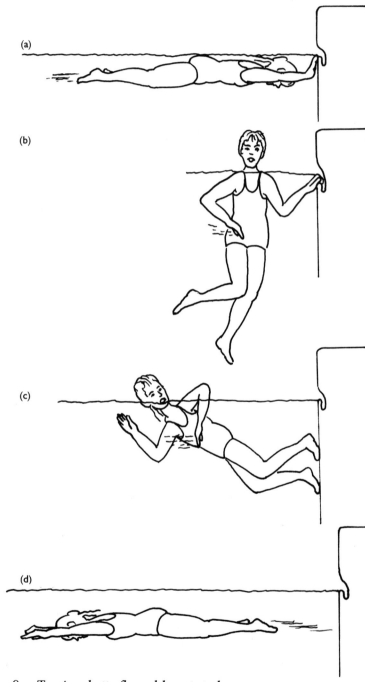

Fig. 9   Turning: butterfly and breast stroke

Breast stroke and butterfly

In these two strokes, turning should not present any problems as you are allowed to use both hands. As you approach the end of the pool, reach out or glide in to touch the side, or take hold of the trough with both hands simultaneously and with shoulders horizontal (fig. 9(a)). Draw your body towards the side and raise the head slightly, so that you can take a breath. Release the side with one hand, allow your shoulder to drop, bend your knees and swing them round towards the wall of the pool (fig. 9(b)). Sink down in the water, place both feet firmly against the end of the pool and thrust vigorously (fig. 9(c)). As you do so, extend your arms, keeping your hands together, so that your body is stretched and streamlined (fig. 9(d)).

Breast stroke

Glide for a few metres with your body completely below the surface. As your speed starts to die away, kick once with your legs and follow with an arm action to help you to return to the surface.

You may wish to experiment with different types of underwater arm pulls to see if you can increase the distance covered before you surface. One popular method is to pull the arms round to hip level and then to extend them forwards in readiness for the first action after reaching the surface. Another way is to pull both arms downwards, bending them as they approach shoulder level and completing the action with a strong backward push which should end at the hips. Again, the arms are extended forwards ready for the next action when you surface, and some part of your head is above water level.

Butterfly

After pushing off into the glide you are permitted to use as many leg kicks as you wish plus one arm action before returning to the surface. Initially, you may wish to limit yourself to three or four leg kicks before using the arm action. Later you can try increasing this until you find the number of kicks that suits you best and does not prove too tiring. Only trial and error will indicate which method is best for you.

The back crawl grab turn

In order to turn while swimming on your back, it is necessary to glance over your shoulder as you near the end of the pool. This should help you to avoid hitting the wall with your head and also to decide which hand will first make contact. As you draw closer, reach out and touch the end of the pool (or grasp the trough) with your leading hand (fig. 10(a)). Rotate on to your front and draw your knees up towards your middle so that you can place the other hand on the wall of the pool or hold the trough (fig. 10(b)).

Now place both feet on the end of the pool, release your contact with the pool wall, and extend your arms beyond your head. As you do so, thrust strongly with both feet (*fig. 10(c)*). This should drive you into a glide. If you do not let your body sink before pushing off you will glide on the surface; if you do sink down as you push off you will glide underwater (*fig. 10(d)*). Whichever method you use, remember to keep your arms extended so that your body remains streamlined, and to bring your leg action in as your speed falls off. Once you are at the surface you can add the arm action as described earlier in this chapter in the back crawl start.

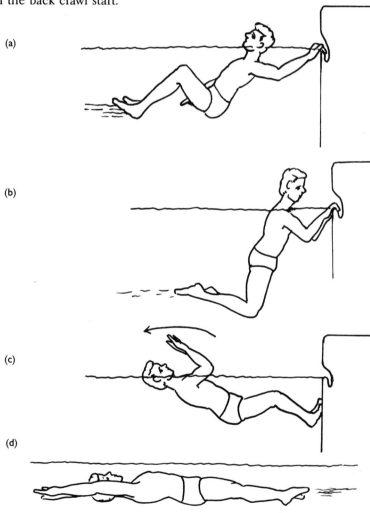

(a)

(b)

(c)

(d)

Fig. 10 The back crawl grab turn

The back crawl spin turn

Later, when you have more confidence, you may wish to speed up the action of the turn by using a *spin turn*. This involves pivoting on the leading hand, drawing your knees up to your chest, and placing both feet firmly on the end of the pool so that you do not need to contact the side with both hands. This will leave you free to extend your arms beyond your head as you push off into the glide position described above. As before, the leg action should be introduced as your speed falls off. Once you break the surface you should pull with one arm, keeping the other one extended. Thereafter the normal stroke cycle should follow.

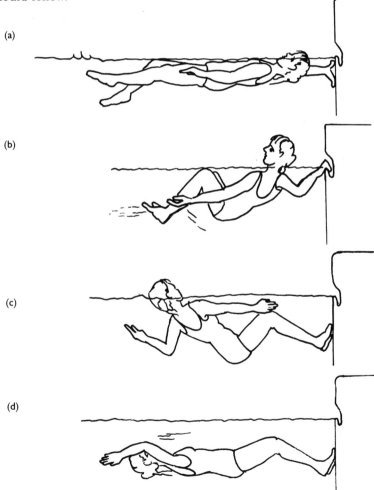

(a)

(b)

(c)

(d)

Fig. 11   The back crawl spin turn

5
Starting a fitness programme

IF you have not undertaken any serious exercise for any length of time, or if you have a condition that requires medical attention and treatment, it is advisable to consult your doctor before embarking on any fitness programme.

Don't let the term 'fitness programme' put you off, however. The aim of this book is to help you to achieve and maintain a higher standard of fitness than before through a *sensible and gradual* build-up, starting with short sessions of around 20 minutes' gentle swimming.

You will be the one who determines the pace at which you progress, for only you will know how you respond to effort and what you can reasonably accomplish in a given time. No two people are alike in their capacity to tolerate prolonged exercise, and with this in mind, advice will help *you* decide what sort of programme suits you best.

Your early visits

On your first visits to the pool, your aim should be to enjoy an easy, relaxing swim and to recapture that pleasant sensation of moving through the water with smooth, well co-ordinated movements. Try to choose a time when the pool is relatively quiet, so that you will be able to swim lengths without constant interruption.

After using the showers, enter the water in any way you choose. If you are unable to dive in, don't be afraid to enter by the steps, from a sitting position on the poolside or by jumping in. Just try swimming a few easy widths or lengths of the pool. Concentrate on breathing in and out regularly, and try to maintain a good rhythm.

Speed is not important at this stage. Just swim for a few minutes until you begin to feel a little tired or breathless, then stop. Provided that it is not too cool, stay in the water and enjoy a short rest at the end of the pool, possibly having a friendly chat with a companion or other pool user, or just breathing deeply until you feel able to continue swimming.

At this point, a change of stroke can add interest and variety to your visit, as well as bringing into play new sets of muscles, enabling others to rest. Many people find that swimming or sculling on the back is a good way to keep moving, and that it avoids breathing problems, as your face should be clear of the water. Again, take it easy, swimming gently and smoothly, feeling the support of the water and trying to establish a steady rhythm.

Aquatic breathing

So far, all of this should not have taken you more than 10 or 15 minutes at the most, and by now you should be becoming used to what is known as 'aquatic breathing'. This simply means breathing out against the pressure of the water while your face is submerged, and breathing in fully as your mouth comes clear of the water.

BOBBING AND BREATHING
However, if you are still not too happy about your breathing technique, the following exercise will soon help you to get the hang of it. It is called 'bobbing and breathing', and is an excellent way of helping you to develop the rhythmic breathing which is so important in all swimming strokes.

First of all, go to the end or side of the pool where the water is at least chest-deep. Place both hands, shoulder-width apart, on the rail or trough. With your face clear of the water, take in a quick but full breath through your mouth. Now close your mouth and, by bending your knees, allow your body to sink until your head and shoulders are completely submerged. Once below the surface, breathe out slowly but forcibly through your mouth and nose (fig. 12(a)). It is important to exhale through your nose as well as your mouth, as this not only prevents water going up your nostrils but also helps to empty your lungs more completely so that you are ready to breathe in once more.

Fig. 12(a) Bobbing and breathing: exhale through your nose and mouth

As soon as you have exhaled as fully as you can, rise to the surface and repeat the process, breathing in fully through an open mouth (*fig. 12(b)*) and then submerging to breathe out through your mouth and nose. Once you have done this four or five times you will find that you start to develop a rhythm and are able to continue for quite a long time without feeling uncomfortable or breathless.

Fig. 12(b) Bobbing and breathing: inhale fully through an open mouth

Ten or 15 repetitions should be enough to help you appreciate what aquatic breathing involves. Later, you should increase the number of repetitions and try to include such practices in the early stages of your swimming programme.

Having practised aquatic breathing at the side of the pool, it is time to practise this technique whilst actually swimming. You should start off by swimming one or two widths (or lengths) of the pool, concentrating on a good breathing technique and smooth, relaxed swimming. Rest and repeat this, aiming to breathe in fully and to exhale through both mouth and nose. After a while you should find breathing during the front strokes becomes more comfortable and that swimming several widths of the pool becomes noticeably easier.

The arm action

Now try experimenting with the arm action. Count the number of arm actions it takes you to swim across the pool or to swim one length. After a short rest try again, but this time press and pull more strongly with your arms, while still maintaining a good leg action. You may be favourably surprised to find that you are able to cover the same distance using fewer strokes. This is because you are concentrating on the propulsive movements and are using a more efficient arm action.

This is an important lesson to learn. Hopefully, too, it is one which you will already have begun to appreciate.

Your first session is almost over now. Finish off by swimming a few gentle lengths of the pool. This part of the session is called the loosening or cooling down swim and it should be swum at a nice easy pace for between 50 and 200 metres. The aim should be to leave the water feeling reasonably relaxed and with the afterglow that comes from enjoyable exercise.

During the first five or six visits to the swimming pool, gradually increase your time in the water from 20 minutes to half an hour or even 40 minutes. At first you may find that the unaccustomed exercise leaves you a little tired or possibly stiff. Don't worry. Your body will gradually adjust as visit succeeds visit; you will be pleasantly surprised to find that your tolerance to exercise improves, and that you can swim further and accomplish more each session.

However, the time this takes will depend largely upon your state of fitness at the outset, your general swimming ability, and the frequency of your visits. If you are able to swim at least three times weekly you can obviously expect to progress more rapidly and perform better than if your visits are only weekly or fortnightly ones.

A swimming plan

It is a good idea to follow some kind of plan during each of your early visits in order to obtain maximum benefit from your swimming. For example:

- a gentle swim for up to 10 minutes;
- brief practice on a second stroke (widths or lengths);
- breathing practices such 'bobbing and breathing';
- general technique practices, either widths or lengths, according to your swiming ability;
- a cooling down swim of up to 5 minutes' duration.

Your immediate aim should be to try to increase the distance you are able to swim without feeling unduly tired or in any way distressed. During such swims you will be helping your body to adapt to aquatic breathing and learning how to pace yourself. Later on you will be given more advice on how to plan further sessions at the pool and you will learn of some ways in which to assess your progress.

Techniques practices

At this point it is perhaps appropriate to explain more fully what is meant by technique practices. As in all sports, the development of good swimming technique demands practice. However, this should not be carried out in a meaningless fashion, but in a thoughtful and purposeful way so that you concentrate on certain aspects of your swimming and then put your techniques into action.

Each of the swimming strokes can be looked at under five headings: poise, leg action, arm action, breathing, and timing (or co-ordination). Sometimes you will be asked to concentrate on just one aspect of a stroke. At other times you will be asked to concentrate on more. Whichever ones you practise, you will eventually be asked to return to practising the whole stroke to see how these 'part practices' have helped you to swim the full stroke better than before.

There are certain important principles which need to be re-stated so that these 'part practices' will be more meaningful to you as you progress.

Poise

You will recall that in all swimming strokes it is important to adopt a streamlined position, or poise, in order to cut down resistance. This means that you should aim for as horizontal a position as possible in order to swim most efficiently.

However, you will appreciate that in order for your legs to perform the appropriate actions they need to be kept below the surface. This means that is is not advisable to swim in a perfectly horizontal position, otherwise your lower legs and feet would break the surface and energy would be needlessly expended. So a near horizontal position is desirable, and all movements within the relevant stroke should disturb this streamlined poise as little as possible.

Leg action

As far as the leg action is concerned, the important thing to remember is that in three of the main swimming strokes – front crawl, back crawl and butterfly – the leg action produces little propulsion for most swimmers, but does provide a balancing effect, limiting the movements of the body caused by the arm actions.

In breast stroke, however, the legs normally provide the greatest source of propulsion; their strong backward thrust, assisted by the arm action, causes the body to move forwards.

Arm action

From this you will have deduced that in all strokes, with the exception of breast stroke, the arms are the main agents of propulsion. For this reason, much time will need to be devoted to improving the arm action if additional propulsive power is to be achieved.

Breathing

Mention has already been made of breathing and what is involved in aquatic breathing. In the forward strokes, you will recall, this means breathing in at some point in each stroke when the mouth is clear of the water, and breathing out through the mouth and nose when the face is returned to just below the surface. As breathing is a vital element in efficient swimming, any time spent mastering the techniques appropriate to each of the swimming strokes will pay sound dividends.

Timing

Lastly we come to timing. This is sometimes referred to as co-ordination, and describes how all the parts of the stroke should be fitted together to produce a smooth, harmonious whole. Good co-ordination comes from purposeful practice and a gradual increase in swimming distances.

It is important to appreciate that developing an efficient swimming stroke not only leads to greater enjoyment and balanced development, but also greatly reduce the chances of developing strain, sprains or cramp.

6
Continuing the fitness programme

IN chapter 5 it was suggested that in the early stages of developing a fitness programme you should try to follow some plan in order to gain maximum benefit from your visits to the swimming pool. The aims of the outlined programme were threefold:

- to encourage you to increase the distance swum, over a period of time;
- to improve your performance in the stroke, or strokes, of your choice;
- to increase your general level of fitness.

If you have conscientiously followed the advice offered, and have swum regularly, you should have found that you are able to swim greater distances – possibly between 200 and 600 metres – than you were capable of in the early stages.

Showing items of swimming equipment you may wish to use during your pool visit

In addition, by spending time practising your chosen stroke, or strokes, you should now feel confident about your performance and should appreciate the importance of 'part practices' as a contribution to stroke development.

Finally, you should tire less easily and feel that your overall fitness has improved through the regular exercise which you have been undertaking. If so, you should now be ready to move on to slightly more demanding swimming programmes.

In this chapter you will be offered advice on how to improve your performance still further. This will be by means of a series of progressive programmes in which a new element will be introduced, the use of *speed swims*. It will be up to *you* to decide when to move from one stage to the next, as only you can decide what pace is most appropriate for you. This will depend on your swimming proficiency, your level of fitness and the frequency of your visits.

There are marked advantages to be gained from swimming in the company of friends or others of a similar standard to you. Not only will this prove more enjoyable than swimming on your own, but it can introduce an element of friendly competition and also encourage you to visit the pool regularly and practise conscientiously.

As mentioned earlier, the format of the programmes which follow is slightly different from the format to which you were first introduced. There will still be a warm-up swim to begin with, but there will also be a number of swims which you will be asked to perform at greater speed than usual. These are called *repetition swims*, because you will be covering, or repeating, the same distance and using the same stroke for each swim.

In addition you will be asked to continue with 'part practices' to help you improve your overall performance of the strokes, and you will be introduced to skills practices to help you swim more efficiently and more economically.

For those practices in which you are asked to swim using arms only, a polystyrene float or swim-buoy (obtainable quite cheaply from most reputable sports shops) will prove a useful aid. However, not all pool managers allow these to be used during public sessions, so before you decide to spend any money enquire first what the pool policy is.

This swimmer is practising the back stroke leg kick using a float

Nowadays most swimming pools have a large clock with a clear second hand, so it should be possible for you to keep a check on the timed parts of your programme. Do remember, however, that if at any time you feel the pace is too much for you, you should take a short rest until you recover. There are no medals for exhaustion!

As in the previous programmes, you will again be asked to finish each session with an easy, cooling down swim so that you end up feeling comfortably tired but relaxed. This is an important part of each session, so do not be tempted to omit it.

Because it is not possible to devise any one programme to cater for both good swimmers and those of only average ability (or a little less), each of the programmes which follow has been set out under two headings, one for swimmers of average ability (or below) and one of those of above average ability. It should be stressed, however, that the distances and the resting times suggested are by no means definitive, and adjustments should be made to take account of *your* level of fitness and swimming ability, in addition to the time available. If, for example, you find you need more or less resting time than the one suggested, you should increase it or decrease it accordingly.

Programme 1

ACTIVITIES	AVERAGE ABILITY	ABOVE-AVERAGE ABILITY
Warm-up swim, own choice of stroke(s)	3–5 minutes	5–10 minutes
First choice of stroke, good speed	25 metres	50 metres
Repeat swim, after rest of 1 minute	25 metres	50 metres
Either sculling on back 1 minute or 'bobbing and breathing' at the poolside	1 minute	1 minute
Pushing and gliding practices from side of pool, aiming for good, streamlined position	2 minutes	2 minutes
Full stroke practice, concentrating on breathing	4 widths	8 widths
Cooling down swim	100–200 metres	200–300 metres

Programme 2

ACTIVITIES	AVERAGE ABILITY	ABOVE-AVERAGE ABILITY
Warm-up swim, using two different strokes	3–5 minutes	5–10 minutes
Repetition swims, own choice of stroke, with rest of 1 minute between each swim	3 x 25 metres	3 x 50 metres
Leg action practices (using a float or with arms extended, thumbs linked)	4 widths	8 widths
Full stroke, concentrating on a good leg action	4 widths	50–100 metres
Cooling down swim, easy pace	4–5 minutes	5–10 minutes

Programme 3

ACTIVITIES	AVERAGE ABILITY	ABOVE-AVERAGE ABILITY
Warm-up swim, any stroke(s)	5 minutes	10 minutes
Repetition swims, aiming at good speed, with 1 minute rests	4 x 25 metres	4 x 50 metres
Arm action practices (using swim buoy or small float between thighs)	4–6 widths	8 widths
Full stroke, concentrating on a good arm action	4 widths	100 metres
'Bobbing and breathing', or sculling	2 minutes	1 minute
Cooling down swim	5 minutes	5–10 minutes

Programme 4

ACTIVITIES	AVERAGE ABILITY	ABOVE-AVERAGE ABILITY
Warm-up swim, second choice of stroke	5 minutes	10 minutes
Repetition swims, first choice of stroke, with rests of:	2 x 50 metres 1 minute	2 x 100 metres 1½ minutes
Diving practice, aiming at a good, streamlined entry and glide	6–8 dives	6–8 dives
Full stroke practice, starting with a good dive and holding the glide until swimming speed is reached	50 metres	100 metres
Sculling, back stroke, or 'bobbing and breathing' practices	2 minutes	3–4 minutes
Cooling down swim	5–10 minutes, any combination of strokes	5–10 minutes, any combination of strokes

Programme 5

ACTIVITIES	AVERAGE ABILITY	ABOVE-AVERAGE ABILITY
Warm-up swim, using two or three different styles of swimming	10 minutes	10–15 minutes
Repetition swims, first choice stroke, with rests between swims of:	3 x 50 metres 45 seconds	3 x 100 metres 1–1½ minutes
Part practices, arms only	6 x 1 width	4 x 25 metres
Part practices, legs only	6 x 1 width	4 x 25 metres
Full stroke practice, first choice of stroke, concentrating on good arm and leg actions	100 metres	200 metres

ACTIVITIES	AVERAGE ABILITY	ABOVE-AVERAGE ABILITY
Turning practice, using any known method of turning, for example spin/throwaway	2 minutes	2 minutes
Cooling down swim, using first choice strokes	5–10 minutes	5–10 minutes

Programme 6

ACTIVITIES	AVERAGE ABILITY	ABOVE-AVERAGE ABILITY
Warm-up swim	10 minutes	10–15 minutes
Repetition swims, own choice of strokes, with rests between of:	4 x 50 metres	4 x 100 metres
	30–45 secs	45–60 secs
Starting and turning practices, using widths of the pool		
Full stroke practice, concentrating on a good start and good turns	100–200 metres	200–300 metres
Cooling down swim, any stroke(s)	5–10 minutes	5–10 minutes

From this point onwards, it is recommended that you devise further programmes of your own, based on a similar format to those suggested above. Remember to include those practices which you have found to be most beneficial in improving your swimming technique, and to introduce variety to prevent each session from becoming monotonous or boring. See chapter 10 on recreational activities for suggestions.

Above all else you should continue to enjoy your visits and to feel the benefit of all your efforts in terms of improved swimming performance, greater versatility and overall fitness.

In the chapter which follows there are some suggestions to help you assess your general progress. However, there is no reason why you should not introduce some of the tests at appropriate intervals during the period over which you are following these programmes.

It should be stressed, that the most obvious 'yardstick' will be personal appraisal in terms of improved fitness and general performance, coupled with your ability to cope with increased physical demands.

Swimming complaints and injuries

Since most people who swim regularly are likely to experience some form of minor injury or complaint, it is important to be aware of what these are and what the appropriate treatment is.

Athletes' Foot

This is an infection which most often occurs between the toes, and it is caused by a fungus which is shed with flakes of skin. It is contracted by walking over surfaces where someone with Athletes' Foot has walked recently. Since the floors in changing rooms and showers are common sources of infection, try to avoid standing around or walking barefoot.

Treatment involves washing the feet thoroughly and then drying fully between the toes with a clean towel or tissues. Afterwards, an antifungal powder or cream should be applied to the affected parts. As an extra precaution, any socks worn whilst the feet are affected should be washed most thoroughly, and shoes and socks should be dusted each day with an antifungal powder.

Verrucae

Verrucae, or plantar warts, are also spread by other sufferers in swimming pools and changing rooms. Should you develop these, consult your doctor at once, as proper treatment is essential. Preventative measures are the same as those for Athletes' Foot, but antifungal powders, etc. are no help. If you have either Athletes' Foot or verrucae, visits to the pool should be postponed until the condition has cleared up.

Sinusitis

This frequently affects those who swim back stroke, and is caused by pool water irritating the lining of the sinuses and causing it to become inflamed. As a result the infected mucus is unable to drain away, causing pain around the eyes, nose, forehead and cheekbones. Should this happen, medical advice should be sought so that either antibiotics or decongestants can be prescribed. In addition, it is advisable to refrain from swimming until the condition has completely cleared up. Wearing a nose clip is a sensible precaution, as this will reduce the chances of water being forced up into the nasal passages.

Eye irritation

The purification chemicals used in swimming pools quite often cause some swimmers to experience eye irritation which may persist for some time after a visit to the pool. Although the use of a proprietary eye wash afterwards will afford some relief, it is sound policy to invest in a good pair of goggles which fit comfortably and are well sealed to prevent water seeping in. However, care should be taken when fitting these. The first step should be to place the eyepiece in positon over the eye sockets; next, whilst holding it there the elasticated strap should be stretched over the back of the head so that the goggles fit tightly and are held firmly in place.

Swimmers' Ear

The main symptoms are itchiness and pain in the inner ear, caused by moisture remaining in the ear canal after swimming. Again, if this complaint occurs it is best to consult a doctor. The use of the ear drops which are normally prescribed for this condition should soon clear up the problem.

Shoulder pain

This occurs mainly after swimming butterfly or back crawl and is usually caused by overtraining. Heat applied to the injured area can help to alleviate the pain. The use of an ice pack as soon as possible after incurring the injury will also help to reduce any swelling. Swimming training should be suspended until the pain has disappeared.

Cramp

This happens when a group of muscles suddenly contracts and becomes knotted, resulting in extreme localised pain. Should you experience cramp, the first thing to do is to leave the water and find somewhere warm where you can sit comfortably. The areas most commonly affected are the arms, legs and toes.

Should the cramp only affect your toes, pushing them upwards to straighten them and then standing on the ball of your foot will help to alleviate the condition. If the cramp is located in the thighs, first straighten your knee, pull your leg upwards and then apply gentle pressure to your knee. Repeat until the condition improves. For cramp in the calf, try straightening the knee and pulling your foot towards the shin. Some people find that massaging the affected part whilst under a hot shower also helps to reduce the painful effects.

A less common but more serious form of cramp is stomach cramp, resulting from specific contraction of the abdominal muscles. More often then not this is caused by swimming too soon after a meal. When it occurs, there is a tendency for the knees to be drawn up to the chest and the head to go down. To avoid inhaling water, tilt the head backwards, take a good breath and scull on your back towards the side.

Since cramp is frequently associated with low salt intake during hot weather or in hot climates, in these conditions make sure you take adequate salt.

7

Assessing your progress

In the previous chapter, reference was made to ways of helping you to assess your progress as you follow a regular programme of fitness training. As was indicated, the first and most logical way of doing this is through self-appraisal. It should become apparent, after you have practised any form of skill for any length of time, that you can perform that skill more easily and with greater confidence. Thus a golfer who has regularly practised chipping can expect this aspect of his game to have benefited, especially if he has followed the sound advice provided in a golfing book or has been having lessons from a competent professional.

In the same way, one of the methods of assessing *your* progress will be through appraising your own performance.

- Can you cover longer distances than before without feeling tired?
- Do you swim further in a given session than you used to able to do?
- Do you feel generally fitter and does your breathing come more easily?

If you can answer any (or all) of these questions in the affirmative, then you can be sure you *have* been making progress during your practice sessions.

However, there are other ways of assessing progress, and in this chapter you will learn how to apply simple tests to gauge your performance. There are three direct methods of doing this: timed swims; time and distance swims; and checking recovery rates.

Timed swims

As the name implies, the first method involves timing yourself over a set distance. If you are able to time yourself over, say, a 100 or 200 metres swim early in your programme, this will serve as a 'yardstick' by which any subsequent timed swims can be compared. By noting the times taken and repeating the test at appropriate intervals during your regular weekly sessions, you will soon have a useful and accurate measure of the improvement being made.

It is best not to attempt timed swims unless you have a reasonably accurate means of checking how long each swim has taken you. If there is a large clock in the pool, with a clear second hand, you should start as the second hand reaches 60 and look up quickly at the clock immediately you complete the swim. Even with good reflexes and perfect vision (which sadly is not given to all of us!) this method will not be 100% accurate. However, it should probably be sufficiently accurate to indicate whether or not you have taken less time than on any previous occasion.

You may feel that this method is unsatisfactory and wish to know to the nearest tenth (or even hundredth!) of a second what your time has been. In this case you will need the assistance of a friend or helpful pool attendant who has access to a reliable stop-watch.

A timed swim. A friend can help you to obtain an accurate time

Assuming that you are starting with a dive from the poolside, ask your helper to give you the starting signal. Stand back from the edge of the pool, and when the command 'Take your mark' is given, step forwards and take up a comfortable starting position (grip the edge of the pool with your feet hip-width apart). After a brief pause, to allow you to steady yourself, the command 'Go' should be given and the watch started.

Dive in and cover the distance over which you have decided to be timed. As soon as you have made the final touch on completing the swim, the watch should be stopped and your time read off.

We suggest that you choose a distance of at least 100 metres for your timed swims, though more ambitious or proficient swimmers may prefer to tackle 200 or even 400 metres.

Whatever you decide, do not exhaust yourself. Keep a steady pace throughout rather than sprinting for the first part of the distance and then fading badly towards the finish. You should feel tired, but certainly not exhausted, and you should recover within a minute or two of completing the swim.

If you do find the swim particularly tiring, it may be that you need to spend more time building up stamina through long swims at a reasonable pace for a while before attempting any further timed tests. In fact, if you restrict your timed tests to one every month or six weeks, this will allow you to develop increased speed and stamina through regular adherence to the type of programme set out in chapter 6.

Time/distance swims

This method of assessment is carried out quite simply by checking to see how far you are able to swim in a given time. For many people 10 minutes should be sufficient, but in the early stages you may wish to reduce the time to 5 minutes and record the distance covered as accurately as you are able – for example, how many lengths of the pool, plus fractions of a length. Converted to metres, this will enable you to see relatively quickly just how well you are progressing.

Although progress in the very early stages may not be exceptional, with regular practice and adherence to your training schedules (which are designed to develop stamina and improve your technique) you should soon find that you begin to make appreciable progress.

As before, a clear wall-clock or a helper with a stop-watch will make it possible for you to time each swim. All you have to do is to remember just how many lengths of the pool you have swum! The policy is the same as for all timed swims. Try to maintain a good speed throughout, and do not exhaust yourself.

Checking recovery rates

Another very useful method of assessing your progress is to monitor your ability to recover from exercise. You can then see how this improves as you follow the fitness programme.

First of all you will need to establish what your usual resting pulse is. This should be checked first thing in the morning, using a watch or clock with a clear second hand, either lying down or sitting up. In this way you may be sure that your pulse will not have affected by any exertion. Even getting up and dressing can increase your heart rate!

The simplest and most usual way to check is by taking the count at the radial pulse on your wrist (*fig. 13*) or the carotid pulse on your neck (*fig. 14*) for 10 seconds. Your pulse rate per minute is then calculated by multiplying this figure by six. If you wish to be sure of your resting pulse, average out your counts over two or three days.

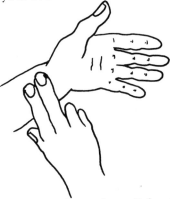

Fig. 13   Take your resting pulse at the radial pulse on your wrist . . .

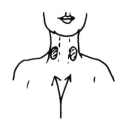

Fig. 14   . . . or at the carotid pulse on your neck

Once you know your resting pulse, you can make use of this when checking on your recovery rate. Simply put, this means that after exercise, for example a brisk swim over 100 or 200 metres, you should take a pulse count and repeat it a minute later. Again, a clock in the pool with a clear second hand can be used, if one is available. Otherwise you will need to have a watch close at hand or a friend who will give you a 10-second count while you take your pulse.

As a general rule, the greater the difference between the two counts, the greater your level of fitness. For example, assuming your first count was 124 beats per minute and your second was 87, the difference of 37 would indicate a good level of fitness.

Conversely, if the second count had been 119, the difference of only five would be a clear indication that you were not recovering from your exertion quite as easily as you should. In this case you would be well advised to spend more time on distance swims to build up stamina and strength, in addition to devoting time to practices aimed at improving your stroke technique and breathing.

After a month or so of conscientious practising you should begin to notice quite encouraging signs in the shape of improved recovery rates. It may well be that you find your resting pulse has steadied and become lower. This is a good indication that your exercise has been doing you good and that your heart and lungs are working more efficiently than before.

There is no need to overdo the pulse counting. Once a week or so should suffice, and if you record the results these will make quite interesting reading over a period of three months or even a year.

In the appendices you will find a useful means of using your pulse counts to determine how hard you should be exercising during your practice sessions. It is recommended that after you have completed a few months of regular swimming (two or three sessions weekly) you begin to use this table to help you calculate the effort level for which you should be aiming in order to gain maximum benefit.

As a result of strenuous exercise the heart rate increases from its resting level to a maximum rate (which is dependent on age and fitness). The tables cover all ages from 20-80. Appendix 1 lists the rates, and Appendix 2 relates them to 60%, 70% and 80% of maximum effort (*see* pp. 91–2).

Masters swimming

Those seeking a fresh challenge could well find it through participation in Masters swimming. Introduced into this country from the USA in the early 1970s, this form of competition has grown considerably in popularity and now involves thousands of British swimmers.

To take part, swimmers must be 25 years of age or over in the year of competition, and in this country they must be registered with the governing body of swimming[1]. Competitors are divided into five-year age bands: 25-29, 30-34, 35-39, 40-44, and so on, up to 80 years and over.

[1] Details of the ASA Registration scheme may be obtained from The Registrations Officer, Amateur Swimming Association, Harold Fern House, Derby Square, Loughborough LEII OAL, or from a official of your local swimming club.

In addition to individual competition in all four strokes and in medley swimming races, team events are also included. These may be for teams of swimmers of 25 years and over, 35 years and over, 50 years and over, etc. More commonly adopted, however, is the system in which the total age of the team members must exceed a given number of years: for example, 120+ years, 180+ years or 200+ years. This system has proved popular with those clubs who, though having few swimmers in a certain age category, are still able to compete by including one or more older swimmers with younger ones in their teams.

Although a number of well-known former competitive swimmers were among the first to become involved in Masters swimming, these have now been joined by increasing numbers of men and women who have taken up swimming in later life. Finding that it is enjoyable to train in the company of other adults, they have joined swimming clubs which offer special times and separate training facilities for those wishing to participate in Masters competition. As a result, many of these men and women have developed into useful competitive swimmers able to acquit themselves well against others in their age bands.

Our own National Masters Championships attract swimmers from many parts of the world. Since the World Championships were inaugurated in 1986 some of our keenest and more experienced swimmers have travelled as far afield as Brazil, Japan, Australia and Canada to compete.

The distances swum for all four strokes are from 50 metres upwards, and there are records at district, national, European and world levels. While most Masters competitions take place in 25-metre pools, the British, European and World Championships are normally swum in 50-metre pools.

Records are kept of the best perfomances from local right through to World Championship level. Though many of those involved in Masters swimming never aspire to become record breakers, they still enjoy the incentive of attempting to set personal best times whenever they compete.

The social aspect of Masters swimming has much to commend it. Those who participate can meet old friends, and make new ones whenever they travel to compete – whether in this country or abroad.

8
Land exercises for improved performance

WHEN you reach the point at which you feel your swimming performance would benefit from land exercises, the following advice should prove helpful.

There are two categories of land exercises for this purpose. First there are general exercises which – though not specifically related to swimming – will help to improve performance, as all muscle groups and joints are used in swimming. Included in this category is any form of exercise, sport or activity which will help to build up stamina. The second category involves those exercises which are related specifically to recognised swimming strokes. The examples given in both cases are those which can be done without the use of equipment or by using simple, improvised equipment.

Daily practice for 15 or 20 minutes at a time, with three times a week as a minimum, will be far more beneficial than lengthy periods of exercise at irregular intervals.

To obtain maximum benefit, exercises which are designed to strengthen muscle groups should be performed with a gradual increase in load rather than an increase in the number of repetitions.

Where there is a particular weakness, for example stiffness in the ankle or shoulder joints, you would be well advised to devote additional time to carrying out the appropriate exercises to increase your mobility or strength. The choice of exercises is wide and varied, but the following selection includes some of the better-known and well-tried ones.

Sample exercises for toning up muscles and improving joint flexibility

Head and neck

These exercises lend themselves to being carried out while the body is in an erect sitting position. This will help to eliminate unnecessary movement and to avoid dizziness.

Keeping your shoulders quite still:

- press your head as far as possible from side to side, trying to touch your shoulder with your ear;

- turn your head to look round as far as possible first to the right, then to the left;
- alternately press your chin into your chest and bend your head back;
- roll your head right round, first in a clockwise direction and then in an anti-clockwise direction (*fig. 15*).

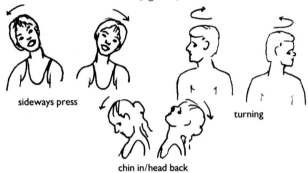

Fig. 15   *Flexibility exercises for the head and neck*

Body

- Kneel on all fours. Alternate the following movements: bend your head down and lift your back into a high arch, then bend your head back and hollow your back into a low arch.
- Standing in an astride position, use a series of rhythmic presses – without bending forwards or backwards – to try to reach further and further down the side of your leg with each arm (10–20 repetitions). Later, swing the opposite arm above your head for increased leverage (*fig. 16*).

Fig. 16   *Side-bends. 'Press', do not bounce*

- Standing astride with your hands resting on the front of your thighs, twist alternately from left to right, at the same time swinging your arms to the 11 o'clock and 1 o'clock positions. Stretch your arms and fingers, look round as far as possible and press your hands back as far as you can.
- Lying on your back with arms by your sides and legs together, first raise the legs approximately 1 cm from the ground, then part them sideways with ankles stretched. Bring the legs together and finally lower them slowly and under control.
- Start from a crouched position with your knees fully bent, knees between your arms, hands shoulder width apart and palms flat on the floor. Jump backwards with the feet, extending the body and legs in one straight line to take up a front support position. From here jump so that your feet are wide apart, then jump back to the front support position and finally return to your crouch starting position.

Arms and shoulders

- Press ups:

a. standing at arms' length from the wall, body slightly angled;
b. again, keeping your body slightly angled, but this time with your hands on a table or chair (*fig. 17*);

(a)

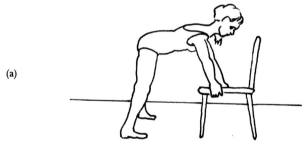

(b)

Fig. 17   Press-ups using a chair

c. in a prone position on the floor, arms directly below your shoulders, but with hips bent;

d. as above, but keeping your body straight.

- Standing with your feet slightly astride, swing your arms alternately forwards and down and then upwards and down. On the upward swing brush your ears with your upper arms and press back as far as possible. Keep your arms straight as you do so.
- Stand in the centre of the open doorway or similar structure and place both hands overhead against the inside of the doorframe, keeping your trunk, knees and elbows straight. Lean forwards as far as possible until you feel your upper chest and shoulders are being stretched. Hold this position for a few seconds and then return to a standing position (*fig. 18*).

Fig. 18 Stretching your arms, shoulders and upper chest

Hands

- Holding a soft rubber ball, squeeze it as hard as possible, then relax your grip. Repeat this, emphasising the squeeze.

Legs

- Perform step-ups, with right and left legs leading alternately:

a. using the first tread of a flight of stairs;

b. moving up to step on to the second tread;

c. finally, repeat first *a* and *b*, holding weights in each hand (for example a squeezy-type container filled with sand or water and sealed).

- Skipping; try different patterns and speeds.

- Taking up a shoulder balance position, start a leg cycling action, trying to make big circles and aiming for plenty of ankle movement.

Feet

As loose, flexible ankles are an essential feature of all good swimming strokes, the following exercises should prove helpful for those with stiff ankle joints.

- Sitting with your back straight, your legs outstretched and your hands behind to support your body weight, practise bending and stretching your ankles and toes.
- Practise picking up a small soft article, for example a sock rolled into a ball, between your toes and the ball of each foot.
- Sitting with your knees bent, reach forwards to grasp each ankle and foot in turn and rotate your foot in both directions.
- As above, but this time hold the lower leg with both hands and shake your leg hard, keeping your foot and ankle joint as loose as possible. Repeat with the other leg.

Stamina

Taking part in any activity for example brisk walking, badminton, jogging or squash – which will get you breathing hard – helps to develop stamina. (Swimming, or course, is an ideal way of making you breathe hard!) Ideally, this type of exercise should be carried out daily.

Poise, relaxation and breathing

Good poise, controlled breathing and the ability to relax those muscles which are not required for propulsion are all essential features of good swimming performance. Here are a few exercises which will help you to develop these features.

Poise

- Stand with your feet astride and reach 'tall'. That means pressing upwards to get the top of your head as high as possible. Swing each arm in turn forwards and upwards whilst swinging the opposite arm backwards. As your arm swings upwards, try to brush your ear with it. Press both arms as far back as possible, keeping them straight.
- Kneeling on all fours, stretch each arm and the opposite leg in turn as far forwards/backwards and upwards as possible. Stretch your feet and hands (fig. 19).

(a)

(b)

Fig. 19 This exercise will help you to improve your poise

Relaxation

- Lie on your back and practise tensing and relaxing each muscle group alternatively. Repeat, but this time tense and relax your whole body.
- Standing in a balanced position, shake each hand and foot in turn, trying to make them feel as loose as possible.
- Standing with your feet a short distance apart, start by dropping your trunk forwards, allowing your knees to bend slightly and keeping your arms as loose as possible. Then swing your arms forwards and upwards to stretch as high and as far back as possible. Repeat 10–20 times.

Breathing

- Stand in an astride position with your elbows lifted above shoulder level, fingertips touching in front of your face. Now press your elbows back rhythmically and slowly three times while breathing fully out. Then fling your arms slowly sideways and back, keeping them above shoulder height while breathing in deeply (10–20 times).
- Whilst practising the arm action of each stroke, as suggested in the next section, it is recommended that the appropriate breathing action be added.

Stroke-related exercises

In the exercises which follow, the aim is to strengthen those muscles which are specifically used in the propulsive arm and leg movements in each of the three main swimming strokes.

Apparatus

The following item of home-made apparatus will prove helpful. Although it is not essential to use this exerciser, many readers will find it a valuable fitness aid.

The apparatus consists of a double pulley or two single pulleys, of the type sold by boat chandlers. This (or these) should be fastened securely to a wall or post just above normal reach height, in a place where it is convenient to carry out your exercises. Strong cord is threaded through each of the pulleys, with a loop at one end for you to hold and a hook at the other end. The cords should be the same length as the height of the pulleys.

In addition, an even number of strong plastic bags will be required. Each contains a kilogram of sand and is tied with a loop (fig. 20), enabling it to be attached to the hook at the end of the cord.

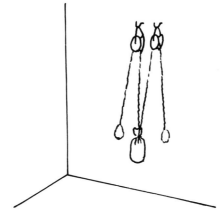

Fig. 20   A pulley exerciser

Use two bags to start with, and add to them later as required. When using the apparatus, remember that it is better to increase the work load – by adding on weight – than to keep increasing the number of repetitions. You should find that between 10 and 20 repetitions are sufficient for each exercise.

Breast stroke

ARMS
- Stand with one foot in front of the other, knees slightly bent and arms forwards in line with your shoulders. Now practise the breast stroke arm action, incorporating breathing. If possible, do this in front of a mirror so you can check the accuracy of your movements.

- Starting in the same position, this time take hold of a loop of your exerciser in each hand and practise the pulling action. Relax and let the weights draw your hands back to the starting position after each pull.

LEGS
- Sit with your legs straight out in front and your toes pointed. Incline your body well back, taking the weight on your hands (resting behind your hips). Now lift your legs off the floor and practise the breast stroke leg action. Rest your heels on the floor after each leg action. (This is also a good way of checking that your leg action is being done correctly.)
- Start by lying on your back. Bring your knees up to your chin and, with your elbows on the floor, support your hips with your hands. Stretch the legs upwards into a 'shoulder balance' position with pointed toes. Now practise the breast stroke leg action in this position.
- Sitting as in the first example above, squeeze weights between your feet, then lift them just off the floor and lower them gently. This is another use of the weighted bags from your exerciser, and you can add to them as you develop greater leg strength.
- Lying on one side with your upper foot through one of the exerciser loops, lift and lower your leg against resistance. Turn on to your other side and repeat with the opposite leg. Remember to increase the weight as required.

Front crawl

ARMS
- Stand with your feet apart, your knees slightly bent and your trunk inclined forwards. In this position, practise the crawl stroke arm action with each arm in turn, keeping the opposite hand resting on your thigh. Then try using both arms in a continuous action. When your arms are working well, try adding the breathing action. If possible, do this in front of a mirror so that you can check the accuracy of the movement.
- If you can obtain two large squeeze-type plastic containers, fill them with sand or water and seal them tightly. Now try this arm strengthening exercise. Holding a container firmly in each hand, and with your arms straight out in front of you and shoulder-width apart, bend your knees slightly and lean forwards (fig. 21). From here pull both arms down strongly and briskly as though making a double crawl arm action, stopping as your hands approach hip level. Repeat this 15 or 20 times, with a slight pause between efforts.

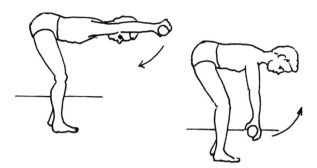

Fig. 21   A good arm-strengthening exercise

- Standing erect with your feet together and a little more than arms' length away from the wall, reach up to grasp the loops of your exerciser. Now pull one of the loops through the same pathway as that taken by your arm when you are performing a crawl stroke arm action. Stop when your hand touches your thigh, and return your arm to the starting position. Repeat with the other arm. Later practise this with both arms working together.

LEGS
- Sitting on a chair or stool, raise each leg in turn with your ankle fully stretched. Lower the leg slowly to place your heel on the floor with your ankle bent.
- Lying in a face-downwards position, raise each leg in turn as high as possible, keeping your leg straight and your ankle bent. Now lower it slowly with your ankle fully stretched.
- Facing a wall, lie on your back so that your feet are just clear of the wall and you can support your ankles in the loops of the exerciser. Raise each leg in turn and lower against resistance.

Back crawl

ARMS
- Standing in front of a mirror with your feet together, practise the back crawl arm action, first using just one arm at a time, then both together. Aim at pressing backwards with your shoulders still further for greater flexibility, and make your recovery an easy, relaxed movement.
- Stand with your back to the wall, about one metre away from it, and with your feet together. Reach up with your arms above your head to grasp the exerciser loops. With one in each hand, practise the back crawl pulling action with each arm in turn, returning your arm to the starting position after each pull.

LEGS

- Sitting on a chair or stool, raise each leg in turn, keeping your ankle fully stretched, and then lower the leg slowly to place your heel on the ground with your ankle bent.
- Lying face downwards, raise each leg in turn as high as possible, keeping it straight and your ankle bent (*fig. 22*). Lower it slowly with your ankle stretched. Repeat with alternate legs.

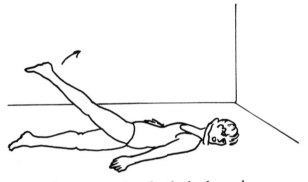

Fig. 22 Strengthening your legs for the back crawl

- With your back to the wall, lie on your front so that your feet are just clear of the wall. Place your ankles in the exerciser loops and raise and lower each leg in turn against resistance.

9
Water aerobics

IT is possible to supplement or even replace exercise on land with water exercises or aerobics, using your swimming pool as a 'gymnasium'. Water not only provides a form of resistance, but has the added advantage that it can be used to balance and support your body weight.

It is not the intention of this book to provide a comprehensive list of water exercises, but merely to offer suggestions as to how to use some of your visits to the swimming pool to practise what is often described as 'water aerobics'. In this context the term 'aerobic' simply means *requiring the uptake of oxygen*. Your heart, lungs and circulatory system will be deriving benefit because in carrying out these exercises you will be using up greater amounts of oxygen than you normally do.

Water aerobics, often performed to music, is safe and fun

But perhaps you are asking: 'Why perform aerobics in water when swimming itself offers such excellent exercise?'. It is certainly not intended that you should neglect your swimming programme for water activities, but rather that your should feel free to choose those water exercises which you decide would be most beneficial to you personally. You should then attempt to set aside 5-10 minutes every other visit (or possibly even once a week) in which to carry out your water aerobics programme.

You may find the following guidelines helpful.

- Do not feel self-conscious about exercising in the water. This form of aerobics is increasing in popularity as more and more people start to recognise the value and enjoyment it can offer.
- Make sure the water temperature is a comfortable one, and in particular avoid exercising in really cold water. This can cause tension and muscular cramp.
- Remember to warm up before exercising, preferably by swimming.
- Adjust the speed of your movements to the strength required. The faster the *speed*, the stronger the *force* will be!
- Start off with just a few repetitions of your chosen exercises and gradually increase the number and the range of movement.
- Keep a steady rhythm going, lively but not too fast.
- Balance effort with relaxation and match your breathing to the movement wherever possible, for example breathing in as you turn and out as you recover.
- Maintain good posture throughout. Make yourself as 'tall' or as long as possible.

It is important that any exercise or routine you attempt should be well within your capability. It is important, too, that you be guided by how you feel. Never persist to the point where you feel overtired, or attempt those exercises which are well beyond your normal range of movement.

For ease of reference, the exercises have been listed under 'benefit' headings to enable you to decide which to select. If, for example, you feel you need to strengthen your abdominal muscles, simply select appropriate exercises from the ones appearing under that heading. (It should be pointed out, however, that many of the exercises described will have beneficial effects on other parts of the body if they are carried out properly.)

Leg exercises

Upward springing

Standing in waist-deep water, bend your knees until your shoulders are under the water and stretch your arms out sideways. Bob up and down a few times, then spring high in the air, using a downward pressure of your hands to assist in the movement. Try to get a good thrust from your feet and ankles. Return to the standing position with a resilient landing.

Leg and arm parting and closing with deep breathing

Stand with your feet together in shoulder-height water, with your arms stretched out in front, palms together. Turn your hands to press sideways against the water, parting the arms as wide as possible with a backward press. Simultaneously slide your feet as wide as you can and breathe in as deeply as you can. Now reverse the movement with your hands turned in. On reaching the starting position press your hands firmly together, squeezing as much air as possible out of your lungs. Later breathe out underwater for added benefit.

Leg swinging

With your feet slightly apart and in waist-deep water, take up a free-standing position (or stand sideways to the poolside and hold the rail or trough with one hand). Start swinging one leg forwards and backwards, keeping it straight and aiming to lift it as high as possible each time. Change to swinging the opposite leg after a dozen or more repetitions.

Note If you hold on to the poolside, it should be possible to increase the range of movement so that on the forward action your toes reach the surface and on the backward swing your heel almost breaks the surface.

Cossack dance *(fig. 23)*

Fig. 23 Cossack dancing is easier in the water!

With the water at shoulder level, take up a Cossack dance stance – i.e. knees fully bent, arms forwards, elbows bent, one forearm resting on the other. In this position practise Cossack dancing (*fig. 23*). (Somewhat easier to perform than on land!)

Cycling

This can be performed while floating on your back and holding on to the rail or trough with both hands stretched out behind the head, or away from the poolside by using a sculling action to keep moving. Practise a cycling action, keeping your legs beneath the surface as you do so.

Pushing and gliding

Stand with your back to the side of the pool, and your arms holding the rail or trough. Lean forwards to place both feet against the wall of the pool, sink below the surface and push off vigorously into a glide. Try to increase the distance by pushing more strongly.

Swimming stroke leg actions

Practise the leg action of the breaststroke, front crawl and back crawl. You can either do this at the poolside, holding on to the rail, or moving through the water holding a float in your outstretched arms: both constitute first-rate leg exercise. The muscle strengthening effect can be increased a) by working the legs harder, or b) by the use of flippers in the front and back crawl leg actions. (*Check that these are allowed in your pool.*)

Arm and shoulder exercises

Water boxing (*fig. 24*)

Take up a free-standing position in shoulder-depth water, with your feet astride, and practise punching outwards into the water with the palms of your hands. Use your arms alternately and punch forwards, sideways, downwards, etc. The faster you punch, the greater the effort required.

Arm bending and stretching

Hold the rail or trough while floating on your front and using a slow, stabilising crawl leg kick. Bend and stretch your arms alternately, so that you move forwards and then backwards. Now push off as hard as possible and see how far backwards you can glide.

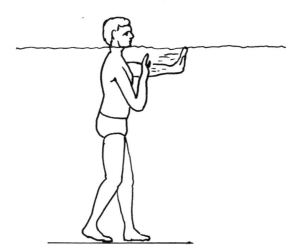

Fig. 24   Water boxing will strengthen your arms and shoulders

Arm parting and closing

In a free-standing position, in chest-deep water and with your arms out sideways, practise closing and parting your arms against the pressure of the water. Then try lowering and raising your arms, always remembering to keep your palms facing the direction of movement.

Double arm pulling

Standing in chest-depth water, lower your shoulders below the water line and walk across the pool using a double front crawl arm action. Pull strongly and then bring your arms out of the water in an easy flinging action to re-enter inside the line of your shoulders. Try to keep the action continuous.

Vertical press ups (*fig. 25*)

Stand close to the side of the pool, in water of about waist-depth and with your chin in line with the rim of the pool. Place your hands on the poolside, shoulder-width apart. By straightening your arms to support your body weight, lift yourself upwards until your chest is above the level of the poolside. Slowly bend your arms and return to a standing position. As this is quite a strenuous exercise, only a few repetitions are recommended.

Chest presses

Standing with your back to the poolside, reach sideways to grasp the rail or trough. From this starting position, gently push your chest forwards with a rhythmic action.

Fig. 25   Vertical press-ups

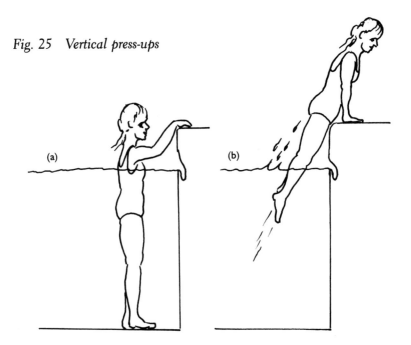

(a)

(b)

Swimming stroke arm action

The arm actions of the breaststroke, crawl and butterfly strokes, performed from a standing position, constitute excellent arm exercise. Stand with feet astride, knees bent and the water at shoulder level. Now move forwards through the water, using a swimbuoy or float between your thighs for support. The muscle strengthening effect can be increased a) by working the arms harder, or b) using hand paddles.

Back exercises

Stretching and curling (fig. 26)

Stretch out in a long or wide prone floating position on your front or back, then curl up tightly to grasp and hug your knees, before returning to the same or another stretch position.

Hang floating

Starting with a good breath, take up a front floating position, stretching out in the water. Let your arms and legs sink downwards and allow your head to drop forwards so that you adopt a floating position with your

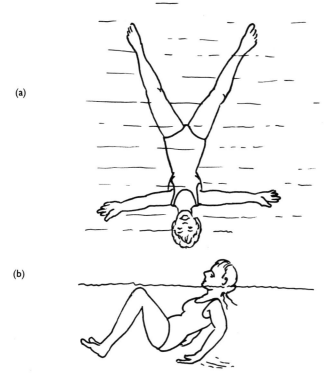

(a)

(b)

Fig. 26 Stretching (a) and curling (b)

arms and legs hanging down loosely. Bend your knees slightly and hold a relaxed position for short periods of time, before returning to another stretched-out position.

Star floating

Push off on your back and assume a star-like shape, reaching outwards with your arms and spreading your legs well apart. In this position, which should be like the letter X, keep your head well back and stretch out on the water. (This may also be done while floating face downwards.)

Abdominal and waist exercises

Exaggerated cycling (fig. 27)

Holding on to the rail of the pool with arms outstretched and back to the poolside, practise a cycling movement with your legs, using an exaggerated knee lift and foot extension.

Fig. 27   Exaggerated cycling

Unsupported curl

Sculling on your back, draw your knees up towards your chest. Hold the position briefly and then extend both legs out until they are straight.

Trunk exercises

Jump turns

Starting from an astride standing position in shoulder-deep water, spring up high and, leading with the shoulders, turn as far as possible, finishing with a resilient landing. Now try jumping in the opposite direction.

Trunk twisting

Stand away from the poolside, in water that is level with your armpits, with your arms out sideways and your feet wide apart. Twist your trunk first to one side and then to the other so that you reach round as far as possible, with your hands skimming along the surface. (This requires plenty of space, otherwise you could have complaints that you are splashing other bathers.) Now bend your knees slightly so that your shoulders are just below the surface, and repeat the movement. Notice the difference!

Scissors

Stand in shoulder-level water with your back to the poolside, feet a metre away from the side and holding the rail with your arms stretched out sideways. Now reach as far as possible over to the opposite side with each foot in turn, separating the feet as widely as possible in a constant scissors movement.

The pendulum (fig. 28)

In deep water (over your shoulders), with your back towards the poolside, reach out sideways to grasp the rail with both hands. Keeping your legs together with ankles stretched, practise lifting them sideways and upwards as near to the surface as you can. Lower your legs and repeat the movement to the opposite side.

(a)

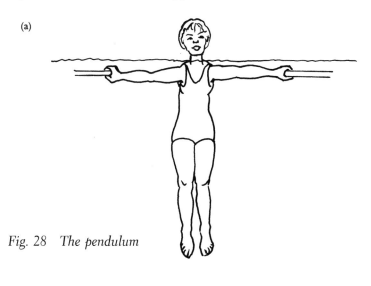

Fig. 28   The pendulum

(b)

Before your visits to the swimming pool it is a good idea to make a list of the exercises which you intend to practise. In this way, you will have an *aide-mémoire* to which you can refer just before each aerobic session. When you have carried out the exercises a few times, you should find it easy to remember what is involved simply by using the names given above to describe them.

10
Recreational activities

IN addition to the enjoyment and satisfaction of performing the more conventional swimming strokes with ease and efficiency, a considerable amount of exercise and pleasure can be derived from exploring and practising various ways of floating, submerging, propelling, turning and rotating in the water. Also, for the more adventurous, there are conventional diving activities to try; while for families and small groups, pair and group activities and games can be great fun.

Examples of such activities are described below. However, there are many more possibilities to explore, all of which are subject to variation with changes of shape, direction, pattern, speed, rhythm, part of the body used, type of propulsion, strength of movement, distance travelled and so on.

According to your confidence and general ability, you might like to try some of the following.

Floating

Try floating on your front and on your back in various shapes, for example in a long shape, a wide shape, a star shape or curled up. In each case, stretch out, curl or twist as far as possible. This applies to the hands and feet in particular.

Sculling (fig. 29)

This is a very useful skill to master, as it can be used to provide propulsion in a variety of ways. In addition, should you wish to rest after a tiring swim or to recover from a sudden attack of cramp, being able to turn on to your back and scull can be advantageous.

The most usual form of sculling is performed in a back floating position, with your hands close to your sides. Keeping your fingers together and with the hands slightly cupped, move your arms in an inward and outward direction, remembering to lead with the palms of your hands. The movement should be a smooth and continuous one, in which your hands move through a flattened figure of eight .

In order to remain stationary, pressure should be exerted in a mainly downward direction. To move your body in a head-first direction, pressure should be applied towards your feet. Conversely, to move in a feet-first direction, pressure has to be directed away from your feet.

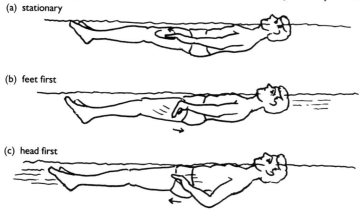

(a) stationary

(b) feet first

(c) head first

Fig. 29   Sculling: stationary (a), feet first (b), and head first (c)

Learning how to scull and discovering how to move your body in a variety of directions merely by making appropriate hand and arm movements can prove to be an enjoyable experience. The sensation of thrust from such sculling movements can also help to develop an appreciation of the way in which propulsion is obtained in the main swimming strokes.

Here is one example.

The tub

Start by floating on your back, using a stationary sculling action. Next bend your knees and draw them towards your chest. By using your hands alternately in a sculling action, rotate first in one direction and then the other.While in the tub position and with your hands held by your shoulders, elbows bent, try using an upward sculling action to submerge. By stopping the action you will find you bob straight up to the surface again.

Rotations

The ability to rotate from the front to the back and vice versa is another very useful skill to acquire. First try doing this from a position on your front. Take up a floating position, then turn your head and tilt one shoulder in the desired direction of rotation. You will find that with the assistance of a gentle sculling action with your hands you should turn quite easily on to your back.

Once there, you can either change to swimming on your back, or just scull if you have become breathless or tired from swimming on your front. Changing from swimming or floating on your back is equally simple. Turn your head and tilt your shoulder in the direction in which you wish to rotate. Once again assist the movement by using gentle sculling actions with your hands.

Treading water

Once you are able to scull, you are in a position to begin 'treading water', i.e. maintaining an upright position in the water. You need to be able to perform a stationary sculling action with your hands to assist the leg action required to keep your head above water. There are three types of leg action which are normally used. The first is a breast-stroke type of leg kick; the second is a flutter kick, similar to the leg action used in front and back crawl; the last one is named the *egg-beater kick*, for reasons which will be apparent when you read the description below. In each method the hand movements should be the same, i.e. with your arms held sideways just below shoulder level, use a stationary sculling action.

Breast stroke leg action

The leg action is basically the one used in swimming breast stroke, but it is carried out in a vertical position (*fig. 30*).

Fig. 30 Treading water using the breast stroke leg action

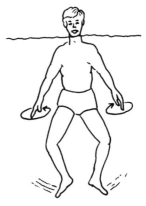

Flutter kick

A modified front crawl action is used, swinging your legs from the hips, so that they pass close together and provide continuous support.

Egg-beater kick

Here the legs move spirally and in opposition to each other. This is the form favoured by most water polo players when they tread water.

Handstands (fig. 31)

Start from a standing position, preferably in water just below shoulder depth. Raise your hands above your head and spring up into a near-vertical dive. On reaching the bottom of the pool place your hands shoulder-width apart, straighten your arms and body and hold a handstand position. Once you are able to do this, take a good breath and try walking about on your hands in different directions, or make a variety of shapes or movements with your legs. With practice it will be possible to balance in shallower water, and finally on dry land!

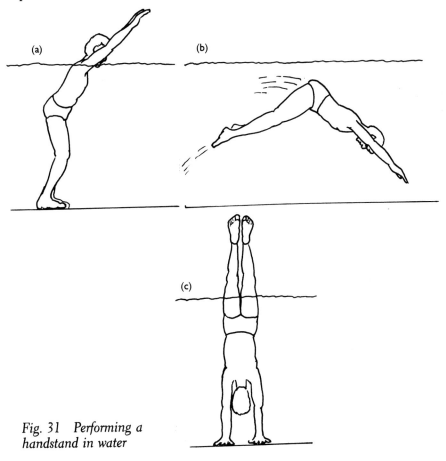

Fig. 31 Performing a handstand in water

Surface diving

There are two types of surface dive which are used to enable a swimmer to go downwards in the water.

Head-first surface dive (*fig. 32*)

Start from a position on the front (usually whilst swimming breast stroke) and make a powerful sideways and backward sweep of the arms. At the same time thrust your head and shoulders down and bend at the waist. Then scoop downwards with your arms to enable you to extend your legs upwards until they are vertical and in line with your body. In this position your body will begin to sink under it own weight. Further scooping movements of the arms can then be used to assist the descent.

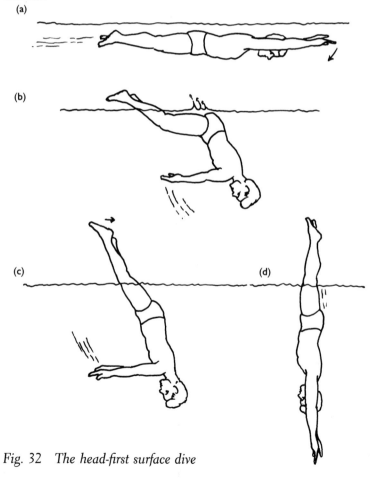

Fig. 32   *The head-first surface dive*

Feet-first surface dive (*fig. 33*)

Begin by treading water above the point where you wish to submerge. Now spread your arms sideways, and make a powerful downward thrust with your legs and arms to force your body high out of the water. With your arms at your sides, allow the weight of your body to make you sink. If you wish to assist the descent or to go deeper, scoop sideways and upwards with both arms at the same time.

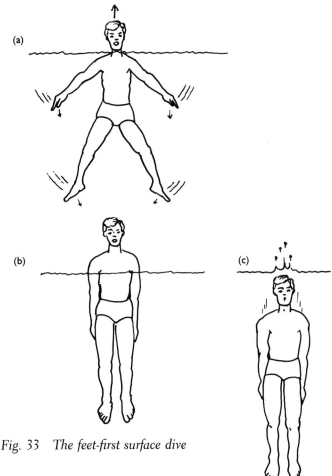

Fig. 33 *The feet-first surface dive*

Retrieving objects from the pool floor

In a depth of water appropriate to your ability, practise surface diving to retrieve objects – such as a rubber brick or one or more weighted plastic rings – and then place them on the poolside.

Somersaults

Forward somersault (*fig. 34*)

From a front floating position, first round your back and draw your knees towards your chest. By dropping your head you will assume a tightly tucked position and start to rotate. Scoop downwards and backwards with your hands to assist this movement until you have completed the rotation and returned to your starting position. (You may find it easier if you start off by pushing and gliding on your front).

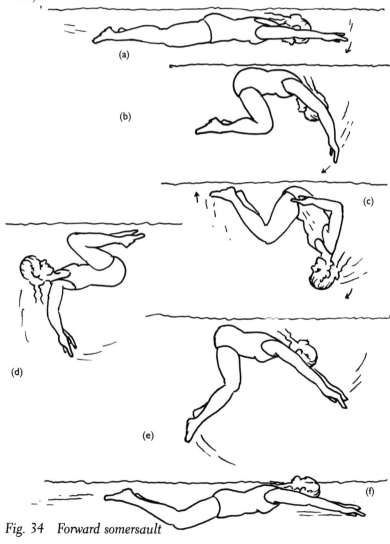

Fig. 34   Forward somersault

Backward somersault (*fig. 35*)

This is carried out either from a back floating or a gliding position. Again, round your back, then draw up your knees and tuck your chin towards your chest so that you assume a ball shape. Lean backwards, lift your feet and scoop upwards with your arms until you have made a complete rotation.

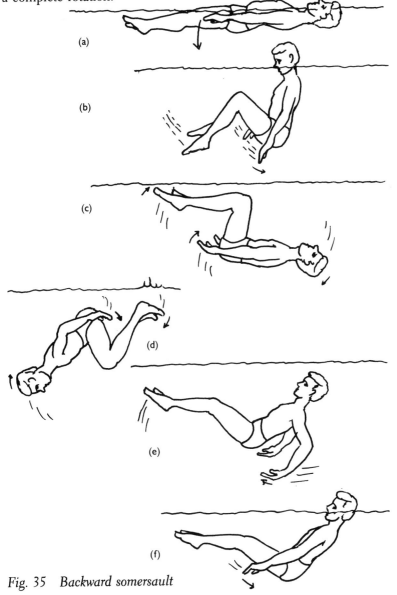

Fig. 35   Backward somersault

Stroke variations

Hybrid breast stroke

This is a combination of breast stroke and front crawl. Start off by swimming breast stroke, and after one arm action and one leg action hold the glide position. Whilst gliding, introduce a strong front crawl leg action to maintain momentum. Then continue swimming breast stroke, each arm pull and leg kick being followed by a glide and several front crawl leg kicks. This is a speedy way of travelling, and with practice you should soon find you are able to swim a length of the pool using very few strokes indeed.

Spiral crawl (fig. 36)

This is swum by alternating between front and back crawl. While swimming front crawl and maintaining a steady leg action, the change to back crawl is made when one arm is forwards, just starting to pull, and the other is by your side. As you pull with the forward arm, rotate on to your back away from the propelling arm. As your body rotates on to the back, take the other arm upwards beyond your head into the entry position for back crawl. As this arm then propels you forwards, rotation to the front crawl follows, with your recovering arm entering the water in front of your head. The whole cycle is repeated.

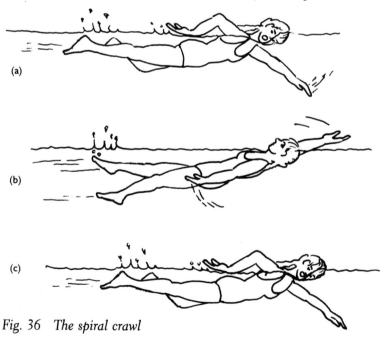

(a)

(b)

(c)

Fig. 36   The spiral crawl

Trudgen stroke

For a change of stroke, why not attempt the old-fashioned trudgen stroke? The arm action is identical to that used in front crawl. The leg action, however, is a scissors-type action. As your forward arm enters the water and begins to pull, and the other arm starts to recover, your hips should be turned slightly so that your body is tilted towards the propelling arm. Whilst in this position, a vigorous scissors kick is made which will propel you forwards. In between kicks the legs trail, but a continuous arm action is used. Breathe in as your body is on its side and your mouth is clear of the water.

Swimming under the water

Many people derive considerable pleasure from the silent world of underwater swimming. As it is important to see where you are going, the use of goggles (or mask, if this is permitted) is recommended to afford you clear vision.

The three most common ways of travelling underwater are:

- using the breast stroke action, but with an extended arm pull towards your sides;
- using the same breast stroke arm action, but with a front crawl leg action; or
- extending your arms as in dog paddle and using a crawl-type leg action.

Practising underwater swimming with goggles or a mask can be a useful introduction to snorkelling or sub-aqua, but do remember not to be too far from the surface when it is about time to take another breath! Remember, too, that if a rapid ascent to the surface needs to be made, this can be achieved by springing up from the bottom of the pool.

As skill develops in less conventional ways of travelling on the surface, it will be found possible to adapt some of these to underwater swimming.

Additional skills

Additional skills that are fun to try are ones similar to synchronised swimming figures. Here are three examples.

Canoeing (fig. 37)

After taking a good breath, push off from the poolside on your front and allow yourself to glide for a short distance. Now raise your head and hollow your back so that your chin rests on the water and your heels are just below the surface. Using a sculling action with your hands close to your hips, propel yourself forwards. By raising your chin so that your mouth is clear of the water, you should be able to take regular breaths.

Fig. 37 '*Canoeing*'

Sailing boat (*fig.* 38)

Start off by sculling on your back, head first, then bend one knee so that your foot is in line with the opposite knee. In this position your bent knee should resemble a triangular sail. Keep sculling and then change legs.

Fig. 38 '*Sailing boat*'

Submarine (*fig.* 39)

Adopt the same position as for the sailing boat, but instead of just bending your leg, raise it into a vertical position, sculling strongly as you do so. Now submerge by using strong upward pressure with your hands, so that your raised leg looks like a periscope. To return to the surface, apply strong downward pressure with your hands.

Fig. 39 '*Submarine*'

Pair and group activities

There are many activities which can be enjoyed in the swimming pool, either with a partner or in groups. The following are but a few suggestions. No doubt enterprising swimmers will devise their own activities to add to the pleasure which may be derived from water play.

Diving between a partner's legs

One partner stands in shoulder-deep water with his legs wide apart, which the other dives or pushes from the side to go between them. The distance can be increased as skill develops so that the approach has to be made by swimming underwater.

Tandem swimming

There are various forms of this. In the first, the front swimmer performs either front crawl or breast stroke while the rear swimmer, holding on to his partner's hips, performs the appropriate leg action (*fig. 40*). Alternatively, tandem swimming can be performed on the back, with the leading swimmer hooking his legs and feet around the upper body of his partner. In this position, both front and rear swimmers use the back crawl arm action. Extra propulsion is provided by the rear swimmer introducing the back crawl leg action (*fig. 41*).

Fig. 40   Tandem swimming (i)

Fig. 41   Tandem swimming (ii)

Towing

Partners can take it in turns to tow one another using a variety of methods, for example using a rope, quoit or other object for their partner to grasp hold of (*fig. 42*). Later, with the 'rescuer' using an inverted form of breast stroke, partners can take it in turns to try different types of hold while towing (under the chin, across the chest, etc.).

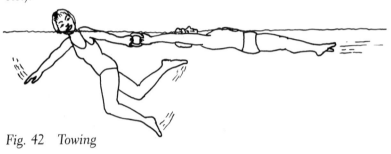

Fig. 42   Towing

Pushing contest (*fig. 43*)

Stand facing your partner, about arms' length apart, either holding opposite ends of a float or pressing your palms against each others. Lean forwards to float on your front, and – using either front crawl or breast stroke leg action – kick strongly to try to force your partner backwards.

Fig. 43   Pushing contest

Water games

Tunnel relay (*fig.44*)

In this game teams of equal numbers stand in lines, with feet wide apart and each player 1-2 metres behind the one in front. On the signal to start, the one at the back of each line submerges to swim through the legs of all the others in the team. As soon as he reaches the front and stands up, the next swimmer follows and so on, until all are back in their original places.

Fig. 44   Tunnel relay

If ball games are permitted in the pool, there are many variations to be explored. Here are two examples.

Pig in the middle

This is a game for three players, in which two players attempt to make as many passes as possible with a ball while the one on the middle attempts to intercept. If the ball is intercepted, the player who threw it goes into the middle and the game continues.

Dribbling relay

For this relay race the teams may be of any size, though small teams are preferable. Each team stands in line on the poolside with the leader holding a ball. The race starts with no. 1 in each team jumping into the water with the ball and dribbling it across to the other side. The ball is then thrown in to the water in front of no. 2, who jumps in to follow suit. As each player finishes, he climbs out on to the poolside. The race is won by the first team to have all players standing in line on the opposite side of the pool.

Large groups

With larger groups, games such as volleyball or water polo can be played across the pool if space permits. The rules can be simplified to suit the pool condition and the ability of the players.

A dribbling relay race. Such group activities are especially fun, and get you fit!

Games without apparatus

There are numerous games which can be played without any need for apparatus. Popular examples are Tag, Follow-the-leader, relay races, retrieval competitions (diving for coins or other suitable objects), and Fewest Strokes contest. In addition, once water skills have been acquired, great fun can be derived by working out activity sequences individually, in pairs or in small groups.

Those who are interested in learning more about water games and activities are advised to refer to the bibliography.

11
An introduction to snorkelling

SNORKELLING is a relatively new sport which is enjoyed by people of all ages throughout the world. With sensible training, any competent swimmer can join in this exciting activity. For most people the attraction lies in the challenge and thrill of exploring the world which lies beneath the surface of the water.

Normally snorkelling takes place in water which does not exceed 15 metres in depth, but great enjoyment can be derived from snorkelling in much shallower water than this.

To take part you do not have to be an expert swimmer. You should, of course, be physically fit. Certain conditions such as heart complaints, ear trouble, epilepsy and asthma may preclude participation, so that if you are in any doubt you should obtain medical clearance before you decide to participate. The following are the minimum requirements you should be able to meet.

You should be able to:

- swim 300 metres on your front;
- swim 100 metres on your back;
- tread water for 5 minutes;
- surface dive comfortably and repeatedly to a depth of 2 metres.

Equipment

If you have ever attempted to surface dive and swim underwater to retrieve objects, you will appreciate that, apart from the fact that the visibility is not always good, the time you are able to remain submerged is limited by the need for air. In addition, travel through the water using normal swimming strokes is not very easy. These limitations can be overcome by using basic diving equipment consisting of a mask, snorkel and fins.

Mask

The eyes need to be surrounded by air to function properly underwater, and this is the purpose of buying a suitable mask. Care should be taken to obtain one which covers the eyes and nose, provides a comfortable watertight seal and has tempered safety glass. A *compensator*, which is a shaped nose piece, is essential. A good test to apply before buying is to place the mask against your face (without fixing the strap) and breathe in through your nose. If the mask provides a complete seal it should stay on your face without support until you exhale through your nose.

Snorkel

This allows you to breathe with your face in the water. A simple J-shaped rubber or plastic tube with a flexible mouthpiece is the best sort to buy. Avoid using a snorkel with a valve, or one which has a table tennis ball to seal the tube when you submerge, for these types can be extremely dangerous.

Fins

Fins act as an extension of your feet and provide you with extra thrust when you are swimming. This extra power enables you to have your hands free for purposes other than swimming. Whatever type you choose, they should be comfortable. Fins which are too tight may cramp, while loose ones may come off or cause blisters. Open-heel types of fins allow for adjustment, but the full shoe type is also perfectly suitable.

Snorkelling for beginners

If you are interested in snorkelling, in the interests of safety the best idea is to join a recognised class or club. Here you will learn the correct techniques from the outset, from people well qualified to provide advice and guidance. However, if you have access to a pool where snorkelling is permitted, or if you are able to swim in safe and warm waters here or abroad, you should find the following initial practices a useful introduction.

It is suggested that for your first attempts you start with the mask only. To prevent misting, rinse it in the water, rub saliva around the face plate and rinse it lightly again. Fit the mask by clearing your hair back, holding the mask against your face with one hand and pulling the straps over your head with the other. If the straps need adjusting, tighten them so that they provide a good seal. Enter the water and try swimming with your face submerged. You should be pleasantly surprised to find that you are able to see everything below the surface very clearly.

If you now feel comfortable with the mask, next try fitting the snorkel. Push this under the mask strap in front of one ear and then grip the mouthpiece gently between your teeth. Swim on the surface, keeping your face in the water, and get used to breathing through your mouth. Look downwards and forwards and try to keep the snorkel upright.

(a) Push hair back

(c) Breathe in to hold mask to face

(b) Place mask in position

(d) Ease strap behind the head

Fitting the mask

Try lowering your head in the water so that some water enters the tube. This should be cleared by pursing your lips and blowing out hard. When you have practised this, wet your fins so that they are pliable and put them on. Enter the water from a sitting position on the side of the pool and try out the finning action. You will find that a wide crawl kick will prove the most efficient method of propulsion, so try this way of finning on your front and then on your back. Keep your hands by your sides and your heels below the surface, and enjoy the sensation of extra speed which fins provide.

Choosing an area of shallow water, you should next practise surface diving, finning underwater and clearing the snorkel on surfacing (but without lifting your face from the water). Should you find that a little water has leaked into your mask, this can be cleared by adopting an upright position, easing the lower part of your mask away with one hand and so allowing the water to drain away.

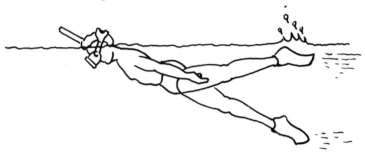

Fig. 45   Snorkelling near the surface

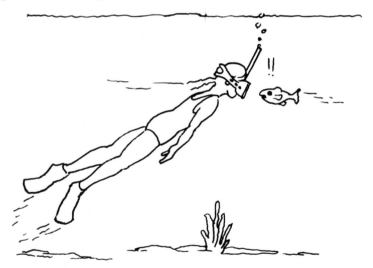

Fig. 46   Snorkelling in shallow water

If you have tried and enjoyed the snorkelling experiences described above and wish to progress further, it is recommended that you join a sub-aqua club where you will be able to learn more advanced underwater swimming skills in safe conditions, from well-qualified instructors.

12
Swim Fit Awards

THE Amateur Swimming Association has introduced a series of distance awards, called *Swim Fit Awards*, to encourage young people and adults to swim regularly and so keep fit.

To qualify for these awards you do not require good style or speed, but just the determination to swim target distances over a period of time. Since there are no time limits for any of these awards, it is entirely up to you to decide what distance to aim for each time that you go swimming. Obviously, however, the more often you go, the sooner are you likely to qualify for an award.

Record cards are available free of charge from many swimming pools or swimming clubs, or from the Awards Organiser, whose address is given at the end of this chapter.

The only requirement is that, after each visit to the swimming pool, you enter the date, the total distance swum and the running total in the appropriate columns of your record card. When you have swum a total of 10 miles (17,600 yards or 16,000 metres), you can apply for the Ten Mile Award.

You can then move on to the 20, 40, 60, 80 or 100 mile awards and – if you are really ambitious – you can progress beyond these, in steps of 50 miles and more, right up to 1500 miles!

The beauty of these awards is that they are cumulative. That is to say, the first 10 mile award may be counted towards the 20 mile award, then the 30 mile award and so on.

Many adults report that working for such awards has spurred them on not only to swim regularly, but to set themselves given distances each time they go. Some have even been known to keep up the good work on holiday by using the hotel pool or local swimming facilities to maintain their weekly target!

Although at first sight the distances may appear excessive, one or two examples will serve to show just what can be accomplished with a little dedication and resolve. If you were to swim three timees weekly and cover around 440 yards (400 metres) on each occasion, it would take you just over 13 weeks to achieve the Ten Mile Award. Swimming 875 yards (800 metres) each visit would reduce the time taken to less than seven weeks. Just imagine what you could achieve in six months, or a whole year!

If you are interested and would like further particulars, ask at your local pool or write, enclosing a stamped, self-addressed envelope, to: The A.S.A. Awards Centre, 11 Kingfisher Enterprise Park, 50 Arthur Street, Redditch, Worcs. B98 8LG. (Tel: 0527 514288.)

You will then be provided with full details of the scheme and a record card to start you off. Attractive costume badges or brooches are available for a nominal charge for each of the target distances. These will be sent to you once you have completed the distance, filled in the details required on your card and sent the appropriate remittance.

When each award is issued, a fresh record card will also be sent to you with the previous cumulative distance entered, so that this can count towards the next distance award.

Why not give this scheme a try? For your health's sake!

Appendix 1
Table showing maximum heart rate by age

(see page 48)

AGE IN YEARS	MAXIMUM HEART RATE (BEATS PER MINUTE)
20	200
25	195
30	190
35	185
40	180
45	175
50	170
55	165
60	160
65	155
70	150
75	145
80	140

1. To calculate your *maximum heart rate*, the following formula provides an approximate figure for maximum effort:
   220 minus age in years
   e.g. for a 58-year-old it would be 220 − 58 = 162.

2. In the early stages of following the fitness programme, it is suggested that you aim to maintain a steady heart rate of 60% of your maximum heart rate. Thus for the same 58-year-old, the aim should be to keep the heart rate at 220 − 58 = 162 x 60% = 97 beats per minute.

3. As fitness increases, the steady heart rate during exercise may also be increased, first to 70% and later to 80%, providing that you are well able to cope with the additional demand.

4. Appendix 2 will provide you with an easy means of calculating what your steady heart (pulse) rate during exercise should be, as you progress through the programme at different percentages of effort.

Appendix 2
Effort rates for various age groups

AGE IN YEARS	60%	70%	80%
20	120	140	160
25	117	137	156
30	114	133	152
35	111	130	148
40	108	126	144
45	105	123	140
50	102	119	136
55	99	116	132
60	96	112	128
65	93	109	124
70	90	105	120
75	87	102	116
80	84	98	112

If your age comes in betweenn any of these, e.g. 37, it is simple to estimate fairly accurately what your pulse rates should be, since they will fall between the figures given for 35 and 40 year olds.

In this case they would be approximately 110 for 60%; 127 for 70% and 146 for 80%.

Similarly, for someone aged 51, the figures would be 101, 118 and 135 respectively.

Bibliography

Aquarobics, G. Baum (Faber & Faber) 1987

The A.S. A. Guide to Better Swimming,
R. Cross (ed.) (Pan Books) 1987

Better Diving, J. Gray (Kaye and Ward) 1985

The Handbook of Swimming, D. Wilkie & K. Juba
(Pelham Books) 1986

Know the Game Swimming, (A & C Black) 1994

Swimming, J. Verrier (Crowood Press) 1985

Swimming For All, D. Sparkes (Pelham Books) 1985

Swimming For Seniors, Edward J. Shea (Leisure Press) 1986

Swimming Games & Activities, A. Cregeen & J. Noble (A & C Black)
1988

Swimming – Going for Strength & Stamina, Marianne Brems
(Contemporary Books Incorporated) 1988

Swimming for Health – The Health Guide, C. Hardy (Health
Education Authority) 1990

*Swimming: Illustrated Teaching Cards for Schools, Colleges, Swimming
Clubs and Parents*, G. Austin & J. Noble (Primrose Publishing)
1987

Personal records

This page has been provided to enable you to record such details as distances swum, timed swims, pulse counts, etc. For that reason, no headings other than the date have been provided.

Date							

Index